COMPREHENSIVE HEALTH FOR THE MIDDLE GRADES

COMMUNICATION & ANGER MANAGEMENT

Kathleen Middleton, MS, CHES

ETR Associates
Santa Cruz, California
1996

ETR Associates (Education, Training and Research) is a nonprofit organization committed to fostering the health, well-being and cultural diversity of individuals, families, schools and communities. The publishing program of ETR Associates provides books and materials that empower young people and adults with the skills to make positive health choices. We invite health professionals to learn more about our high-quality publishing, training and research programs by contacting us at P.O. Box 1830, Santa Cruz, CA 95061-1830, (800) 321-4407.

Kathleen Middleton, MS, CHES, is editor-in-chief at ETR Associates. She is a nationally recognized expert in the field of school health education and has been involved at local, state and national levels. She taught middle school health education for 10 years before entering full-time into educational curricula and materials development. She was the editor of ETR Associates' Contemporary Health Series and has been primary author or editor for more than 30 health education curricula. She directed the development, evaluation and dissemination of *Growing Healthy* for the National Center for Health Education and is coauthor, with Dr. Marion Pollock, of a widely used college textbook, *School Health Instruction: The Elementary and Middle School Years.*

Comprehensive Health for the Middle Grades
Abstinence
Communication and Anger Management
Consumer Health
Drugs
Environmental Health
Family Relationships
Fitness and Hygiene
HIV and STD
Injury Prevention
Nutrition and Body Image
Peer Relationships
Puberty and Reproduction
Self-Esteem
Tobacco
Violence

Printed in the United States of America

10 9 8 7 6 5 4 3 2

Series Editor: Kathleen Middleton

Text design: Graphic Elements

Illustrations: Nina Paley

Title No. H567

CONTENTS

CONTENTS

CONTENTS

Contents

CONTENTS

ACKNOWLEDGMENTS

Comprehensive Health for the Middle Grades was made possible with the assistance of dedicated curriculum developers, teachers and health professionals. This program evolved from *Into Adolescence*, the middle school component of the *Contemporary Health Series*. The richness of this new program is demonstrated by the pool of talented professionals involved in both the original and the new versions.

Developers

Dale W. Evans, HSD, CHES
Health Science Dept.
California State University, Long Beach

Emogene Fox, EdD, CHES
Health Education Dept.
University of Central Arkansas, Conway

Mary Steckiewicz Garzino, MEd
Educator and Developer of Curriculum
Chicago, Illinois

Susan Giarratano, EdD
Health Science Dept.
California State University, Long Beach

Catherine S. Golliher, PhD
Walter Reed Middle School
North Hollywood, California

Janet L. Henke
Old Court Middle School
Randallstown, Maryland

Russell G. Henke, MEd
Montgomery County Public Schools
Rockville, Maryland

Jon W. Hisgen, MS
Pewaukee Public Schools
Pewaukee, Wisconsin

Anita Hocker, EdD
School Board of Sarasota County
Sarasota, Florida

Lisa K. Hunter, PhD
Health & Education Communication Consultants
Berkeley, California

Susan J. Laing, MS, CHES
Dept. of Veterans Affairs Medical Center
Birmingham, Alabama

Carole McPherson, MA
Mission Hill Junior High School
Santa Cruz, California

Jory Post, MA
Happy Valley Elementary School
Santa Cruz, California

Judith K. Scheer, EdS, CHES
Contra Costa County Office of Education
Walnut Creek, California

Mae Waters, PhD, CHES
Florida Dept. of Education
Tallahassee, Florida

Dale Zevin, MA
Educational Consultant
Santa Cruz, California

Reviewers and Consultants

Robinette J. Bacon
State Dept. of Education
Carson City, Nevada

Debbie Baker, MS
Wilbur D. Mills Education Cooperative
Beebe, Arkansas

Ann Bialy
Santa Rita Union School District
Salinas, California

David Birch, PhD, CHES
Dept. of Applied Health Science
Indiana University, Bloomington

Judy Boswell, RN, MS, CHES
Health Education Dept.
University of Central Arkansas, Conway

Carol I. Bratton, MA
Walters Junior High School
Fremont, California

Elizabeth Bumpus, MEd
Sarasota County Health Dept.
Sarasota, Florida

Nanette Burton, MA
Consultant and Family Therapist
Monte Vista, Colorado

Marianne Bush
Pajaro Valley Unified School District
Aptos, California

Diane Davis
D. Davis Consulting and Counseling
Bellevue, Washington

Donald L. Calitri, EdD, CHES
Eastern Kentucky University
Richmond, Kentucky

Peggy J. Campbell, MA
Cabell County Public Schools
Huntington, West Virginia

Cal Deason, MA
Aptos Junior High School
Aptos, California

David L. Delongchamp
Northside School
Cool, California

Lisa Ann DiPlacido, MS
Greater Erie Community Action Committee
Erie, Pennsylvania

Jon Dore
Education Consultant
Aptos, California

Claire Drew, RN, MSED
School Nurse/Health Curriculum Coordinator
Gorham, Maine

Kalvin Engleberg, MA
Oakland County Health Dept.
Pontiac, Michigan

Joyce V. Fetro, PhD, CHES
San Francisco Unified School District
San Francisco, California

Cathy Fraser
Sylvandale Middle School
San Jose, California

ACKNOWLEDGMENTS

Jaine Gilbert
King Junior High School
Berkeley, California

Gregory D. Gordon
American Indian Education and Cultural Organization
Martinez, California

Sue Gruber
Petaluma Old Adobe School
Petaluma, California

Robin McFarland Gysin
Consumer Affairs Coordinator
Santa Cruz County, California

Heidi Hataway, MS, RD
Nutritionist
University of Alabama at Birmingham

Paul G. Heller, MA, MFA
Benicia High School
Benicia, California

Anita Howard
Comprehensive Health Consultant
New Lenox, Illinois

Betty Hubbard, EdD, CHES
Health Education Dept.
University of Central Arkansas, Conway

Nina M. Jackson, MS
Fort Worth Independent School District
Fort Worth, Texas

Pam Jones, MEd
Clarksville School District
Clarksville, Arkansas

Vicki Jordan, MA
Newport Middle School
Newport, Oregon

Freya H. Kaufman, MA, CHES
Executive Consultant for School Health Programs
New York Academy of Medicine

Suzanne Kordesh, MPH, RD
Nutrition Consultant
Berkeley, California

Dan Kuhl
Wisconsin School for the Visually Handicapped
Janesville, Wisconsin

Edgar Leon, PhD
Michigan Dept. of Education
Lansing, Michigan

Linda Loushin
Junction Avenue School
Livermore, California

David M. Macrina, PhD
Dept. of Health Education and Physical Education
University of Alabama at Birmingham

Donnie McBride
Windburn Junior High
Lexington, Kentucky

Linda McDaniel, MS
Van Buren Middle School
Van Buren, Arkansas

Robert McDermott, PhD
College of Public Health
University of South Florida, Tampa

Warren McNab, PhD
Health Education Dept.
University of Nevada at Las Vegas

Louise K. Mann, MEd, MAR
Renbrook School
West Hartford, Connecticut

Eloise L. Miller, MEd
Anoka-Hennepin District #11
Anoka, Minnesota

Cheryl Mills, PHN
Soquel Elementary School District
Capitola, California

Ken Montoya
Pasadena Unified School District
Pasadena, California

Iris A. Mudd, MEd
Stokes County School District
Sandy Ridge, North Carolina

Sue Myers, MEd
Pine Strawberry School District
Pine, Arizona

Sandy Nichols, RN, MEd
State Dept. of Elementary and Secondary Education
Jefferson City, Missouri

Joanne Owens-Nauslar, EdD
Nebraska State Dept. of Education
Lincoln, Nebraska

John Pence, PhD
Newport Middle School
Newport, Oregon

Marcia Quackenbush, MS, MFCC
AIDS Health Project
University of California, San Francisco

Chuck Regin, PhD
Health Education Dept.
University of Nevada, Las Vegas

Norma Riccobuono
La Paloma High School
Brentwood, California

Fay Catlett Sady, MPH
County Office of Education
Santa Cruz, California

Paul M. Santasieri, MA
Pinelands Regional High School District
Tuckerton, New Jersey

Murry Schekman
E. A. Hall Middle School
Watsonville, California

Barbara Sheffield, MS
Whitewater Public Schools
Whitewater, Wisconsin

William Shuey
Center for Self-Esteem
Santa Cruz, California

Janet L. Sola, PhD
YWCA of the U.S.A.
New York, New York

Susan K. Telljohann, HSD
Dept. of Health Promotion and Human Performance
University of Toledo

Marcia Thompson
New Brighton Middle School
Soquel, California

Cathy Valentino
Simon and Schuster
New York, New York

Cynthia M. Walczak
New Mexico Dept. of Health—Family Planning
Santa Fe, New Mexico

Jeanne Williams
New York City Board of Education
Brooklyn, New York

Nancy Winkler, MSE
Human Growth and Development Coordinator
Oshkosh, Wisconsin

Sandra Whitney
King Estates Junior High School
Oakland, California

Glenda M. Wood
Impact Communication, Inc.
Tallahassee, Florida

Patricia Zylius
Writer
Santa Cruz, California

Program Overview

COMPONENTS

PROGRAM GOAL

Students will acquire the necessary skills and information to make healthy choices.

Comprehensive Health for the Middle Grades consists of 15 Teacher/Student Resource books, 10 of which have corresponding *Health Facts* books and sets of posters. The *Think, Choose, Act Healthy* book rounds out the basic program. Note that there are other ancillary items available, such as additional *Health Facts* books.

- **Teacher/Student Resource Books**—These 15 books address key health topics, content and issues for middle school students. All teacher/student information, instructional process, assessment tools and student activity masters for the particular topic are included in each book.

- *Health Facts* **Books**—These reference books provide clear, concise background information to support the resource books.

- *Think, Choose, Act Healthy*—This book provides more than 130 reproducible student activities that work hand in hand with the teacher/student resource books. They will challenge students to think and make their own personal health choices.

- **Comprehensive Health Poster Series**—These 40 instructional posters inform and provoke critical student thinking. They are a high-interest way to present simple to complex health issues.

- *Spanish Resource Supplement*—The objectives, purposes, main points, vocabulary, student activity sheets and family letters from the 15 resource books are contained in this book.

PROGRAM OVERVIEW

ORGANIZATION

Comprehensive Health for the Middle Grades		
Components		
Resource Books	**Health Facts Books**	**Posters***
Abstinence	Abstinence	4 Abstinence Posters
Drugs	Drugs	4 Drugs Posters
Fitness and Hygiene	Fitness	4 Fitness and Hygiene Posters
HIV and STD	STD	4 HIV and STD Posters
Injury Prevention	Injury Prevention	4 Injury Prevention Posters
Nutrition and Body Image	Nutrition and Body Image	4 Nutrition and Body Image Posters
Puberty and Reproduction	Sexuality	4 Puberty and Reproduction Posters
Self-Esteem	Self-Esteem and Mental Health	4 Self-Esteem Posters
Tobacco	Tobacco	4 Tobacco Posters
Violence	Violence	4 Violence Posters

Additional Resources
Resource Books
Communication and Anger Management
Consumer Health
Environmental Health
Family Relationships
Peer Relationships
Health Facts Books
Disease
Environmental and Community Health
HIV

*Each content area includes: "Myth and Fact," "Dictionary of Life," "In Your Face," and "Fred and Frieda" posters.

PROGRAM OVERVIEW

SEQUENCING

Comprehensive Health for the Middle Grades is a flexible program that will allow teachers to tailor their instruction to their own students' needs and interests. For schools planning to spiral health instruction through the middle grades, the following sequence is suggested.

Please note that this is a suggested sequence. The program is designed to be flexible and meant to be arrayed in accordance with individual school needs. It may be that a different sequence is more appropriate for your school setting.

Subject Placement by Grade Level
Grade 6
Peer Relationships
Tobacco
Family Relationships
Communication and Anger Management
Environmental Health
Grade 7
Self-Esteem
Drugs
Fitness and Hygiene
Puberty and Reproduction*
Injury Prevention
Grade 8
Violence
Abstinence
Nutrition and Body Image
Consumer Health
HIV and STD

*Puberty lessons can be taught separately as early as 4th grade.

PROGRAM OVERVIEW

SUBJECT INTEGRATION

Here are suggestions for integrating health instruction into other subjects in the middle school curriculum.

Subject	Integration Suggestion	Alternate Suggestion
Language Arts	Self-Esteem Abstinence Communication and Anger Management	Violence Peer Relationships
Science	Puberty and Reproduction* Environmental Health Drugs HIV and STD Tobacco	Nutrition and Body Image Injury Prevention Fitness Consumer Health
Home Economics	Nutrition and Body Image Consumer Health	Puberty and Reproduction* Abstinence Family Relationships
Social Issues	Peer Relationships Violence Family Relationships	Drugs Tobacco Communication and Anger Management Environmental Health HIV and STD Self-Esteem
Physical Education	Fitness and Hygiene	

*Puberty lessons can be taught separately as early as 4th grade.

PROGRAM OVERVIEW

TEACHING STRATEGIES

Each resource book is designed so you can easily find the instructional content, process and skills. You can spend more time on teaching and less on planning. Special tools are provided to help you challenge your students, reach out to their families and assess student success.

A wide variety of learning opportunities is provided in each book to increase interest and meet the needs of different kinds of learners. Many are interactive, encouraging students to help each other learn. The **31** teaching strategies can be divided into 4 categories based on educational purpose. They are Informational, Creative Expression, Sharing Ideas and Opinions and Developing Critical Thinking. Descriptions of the teaching strategies are found in the appendix.

Providing Key Information

Students need information before they can move to higher-level thinking. This program uses a variety of strategies to provide the information students need to take actions for health. Strategies include:

- anonymous question box
- current events
- demonstrations
- experiments
- games and puzzles
- guest speakers
- information gathering
- interviewing
- oral presentations

Encouraging Creative Expression

Creative expression provides the opportunity to integrate language arts, fine arts and personal experience into learning. It also allows students the opportunity to demonstrate their understanding in ways that are unique to them. Creative expression encourages students to capitalize on their strengths and their interests. Strategies include:

- artistic expression
- creative writing
- dramatic presentations
- roleplays

TEACHING STRATEGIES

Sharing Ideas, Feelings and Opinions

In the sensitive area of health education, providing a safe atmosphere in which to discuss a variety of opinions and feelings is essential. Discussion provides the opportunity to clarify misinformation and correct misconceptions. Strategies include:

- brainstorming
- class discussion
- clustering
- continuum voting
- dyad discussion
- family discussion
- forced field analysis
- journal writing
- panel discussion
- self-assessment
- small groups
- surveys and inventories

Developing Critical Thinking

Critical thinking skills are crucial if students are to adopt healthy behaviors. Healthy choices necessitate the ability to become independent thinkers, analyze problems and devise solutions in real-life situations. Strategies include:

- case studies
- cooperative learning groups
- debates
- factual writing
- media analysis
- personal contracts
- research

PROGRAM OVERVIEW

SKILLS INFUSION

Studies of high-risk children and adolescents show that certain characteristics are common to children who succeed in adverse situations. These children are called resilient. Evaluation of educational programs designed to build resiliency has shown that several elements are important for success. The most important is the inclusion of activities designed to build personal and social skills.

Throughout each resource book, students practice skills along with the content addressed in the activities. Activities that naturally infuse personal and social skills are identified.

- **Communication**—Students with effective communication skills are able to express thoughts and feelings, actively listen to others, and give clear verbal and nonverbal messages related to health or any other aspect of their lives.

- **Decision Making**—Students with effective decision-making skills are able to identify decision points, gather information, and analyze and evaluate alternatives before they take action. This skill is important to promote positive health choices.

- **Assertiveness**—Students with effective assertiveness skills are able to resist pressure and influence from peers, advertising or others that may be in conflict with healthy behavior. This skill involves the ability to negotiate in stressful situations and refuse unwanted influences.

- **Stress Management**—Students with effective stress-management skills are able to cope with stress as a normal part of life. They are able to identify situations and conditions that produce stress and adopt healthy coping behaviors.

- **Goal Setting**—Students with effective goal-setting skills are able to clarify goals based on their needs and interests. They are able to set realistic goals, identify the sub-steps to goals, take action and evaluate their progress. They are able to learn from mistakes and change goals as needed.

PROGRAM OVERVIEW

WORKING WITH FAMILIES AND COMMUNITIES

A few general principles can help you be most effective in teaching about health:

- Establish a rapport with your students, their families and your community.
- Prepare yourself so that you are comfortable with the content and instructional process required to teach about communication and anger management successfully.
- Be aware of state laws and guidelines established by your school district that relate to health.
- Invite parents and other family members to attend a preview of the materials.

Some lessons include letters about the units and activities to be completed at home. Family involvement improves student learning. Encourage family members and other volunteers to help you in the classroom as you teach these activities.

It is always important to be sensitive to the diverse family situations of your students. Be alert to family situations that may make completion of an assignment difficult for a student and make alternate arrangements as necessary.

THE COMMUNICATION AND ANGER MANAGEMENT RESOURCE BOOK

WHY TEACH ABOUT COMMUNICATION AND ANGER MANAGEMENT?

Effective communication with friends, family, coworkers and others is a lifelong process. People learn about communicating and expressing emotions in complex ways. This learning involves a variety of influences, experiences and interactions, which arise from familial, cultural, geographic, educational, legal, religious and personal backgrounds. Self-esteem also plays a role in this process.

The way we express emotions communicates our feelings to other people. Everyone experiences emotions. Emotions are highly personal, and each of us draws upon our own experiences to help us shape our understanding of them. As we grow older, we learn how to deal with our feelings and to express emotions in ways that help us relate and interact more effectively.

Expressing strong emotions such as anger and fear helps relieve the accompanying tension. Learning how to express strong emotions in socially acceptable ways is an important step in the maturation process.

Adolescents and Communication

Adolescents who do not know how to communicate often cannot find constructive ways to release their anger, frustration or even good feelings. This can increase stress and lower self-esteem.

When communication of feelings, particularly anger and frustration, are misinterpreted, the pressure mounts, which may lead to inappropriate expressions of these strong emotions. Violent behavior is often linked to frustration and anger. Fear and anger stimulate the secretion of adrenalin into the bloodstream, resulting in a physical reaction. The ability to communicate or express these emotions is important not only to mental health but to our physical health as well.

Remember to approach lessons about communication with sensitivity to students' backgrounds, experiences and vulnerability to group expectations and pressures. Make every effort to understand family and cultural influences, as well as the kinds of peer pressure students may face.

Each person reacts differently to various life situations. The things that cause one person to feel a certain emotion will not necessarily cause another person to experience the same emotion. The units in this curriculum are designed to help students gain effective communication skills so they can express their personal feelings in socially acceptable ways and learn to appreciate the unique feelings of the other people in their widening circle of experience.

THE COMMUNICATION AND ANGER MANAGEMENT RESOURCE BOOK

WHY TEACH ABOUT COMMUNICATION AND ANGER MANAGEMENT?

Background Information About Communication and Anger Management

Instant Expert sections throughout this book give you all the information you need to teach each unit.

THE COMMUNICATION AND ANGER MANAGEMENT RESOURCE BOOK

OBJECTIVES

Students Will Be Able to:

Unit 1: Ways of Communicating
- Define communication.
- Compare 3 types of communication.

Unit 2: Communication Sense
- Explain the importance of the senses in communication.

Unit 3: Communication Troubles
- Demonstrate techniques for overcoming barriers to communication.

Unit 4: Emotions and Communication
- Conclude that emotions are very personal feelings, expressed differently from person to person.

Unit 5: Fear and Anger
- Explain the stress response.
- Describe appropriate ways to express anger.

Unit 6: Emotions Booklets
- Illustrate various expressions of emotions.

Unit 7: You and Your Feelings About Others
- Analyze common problems around communication in order to provide useful advice.

ANATOMY OF A UNIT

PREPARING TO TEACH

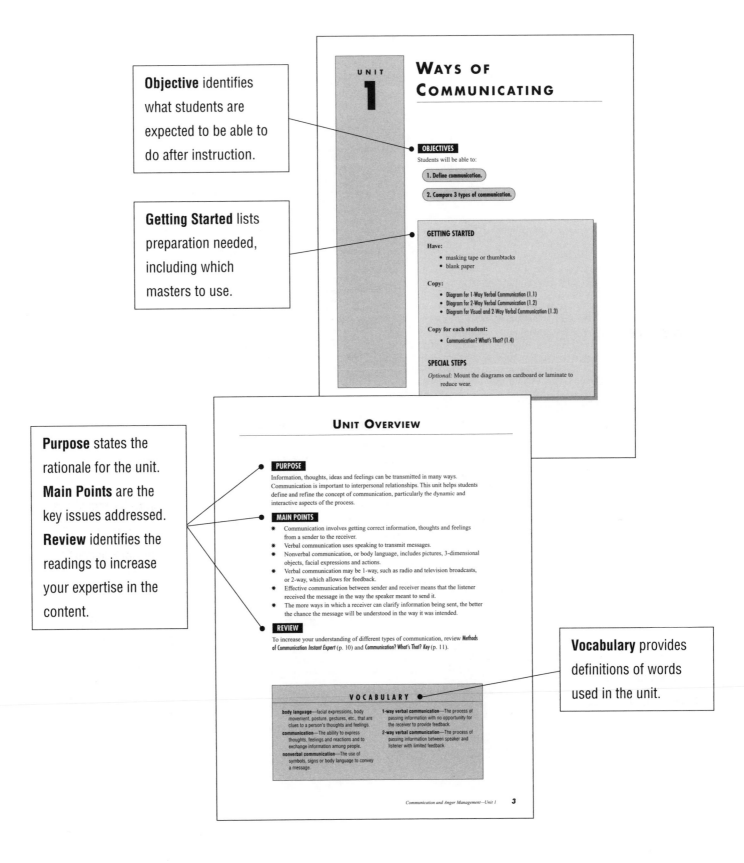

Objective identifies what students are expected to be able to do after instruction.

Getting Started lists preparation needed, including which masters to use.

Purpose states the rationale for the unit. **Main Points** are the key issues addressed. **Review** identifies the readings to increase your expertise in the content.

Vocabulary provides definitions of words used in the unit.

UNIT
1

WAYS OF COMMUNICATING

OBJECTIVES

Students will be able to:

1. Define communication.

2. Compare 3 types of communication.

GETTING STARTED

Have:

- masking tape or thumbtacks
- blank paper

Copy:

- Diagram for 1-Way Verbal Communication (1.1)
- Diagram for 2-Way Verbal Communication (1.2)
- Diagram for Visual and 2-Way Verbal Communication (1.3)

Copy for each student:

- Communication? What's That? (1.4)

SPECIAL STEPS

Optional: Mount the diagrams on cardboard or laminate to reduce wear.

UNIT OVERVIEW

PURPOSE

Information, thoughts, ideas and feelings can be transmitted in many ways. Communication is important to interpersonal relationships. This unit helps students define and refine the concept of communication, particularly the dynamic and interactive aspects of the process.

MAIN POINTS

* Communication involves getting correct information, thoughts and feelings from a sender to the receiver.
* Verbal communication uses speaking to transmit messages.
* Nonverbal communication, or body language, includes pictures, 3-dimensional objects, facial expressions and actions.
* Verbal communication may be 1-way, such as radio and television broadcasts, or 2-way, which allows for feedback.
* Effective communication between sender and receiver means that the listener received the message in the way the speaker meant to send it.
* The more ways in which a receiver can clarify information being sent, the better the chance the message will be understood in the way it was intended.

REVIEW

To increase your understanding of different types of communication, review *Methods of Communication Instant Expert* (p. 10) and *Communication? What's That? Key* (p. 11).

VOCABULARY

body language—facial expressions, body movement, posture, gestures, etc., that are clues to a person's thoughts and feelings.
communication—The ability to express thoughts, feelings and reactions and to exchange information among people.
nonverbal communication—The use of symbols, signs or body language to convey a message.

1-way verbal communication—The process of passing information with no opportunity for the receiver to provide feedback.
2-way verbal communication—The process of passing information between speaker and listener with limited feedback.

ANATOMY OF A UNIT

TEACHING THE ACTIVITIES

Instant Expert pages provide concise background information for you. They follow each unit.

METHODS OF COMMUNICATION

I N S T A N T   E X P E R T

Communication is a process by which information is exchanged between and among individuals through a common system of symbols, signs or behaviors. Most communication is achieved verbally. Verbal communication can be *1-way* or *2-way*.

1-way verbal communication: In 1-way communication, information is passed from person to person with no opportunity for feedback. Most television and radio broadcasts are examples of 1-way communication. (There are exceptions, such as call-in radio and TV shows.)

This type of communication does not allow the listener to ask the speaker questions that might clarify the message. It does not allow for interactions between and among people. When communication is 1-way, the message received may *not* be the message the speaker intended.

2-way verbal communication: Using this type of communication means that information passes orally from person to person with limited feedback. The receiver can ask for oral (verbal) clarification; he or she can ask questions of the speaker.

2-way verbal and visual communication: Information is passed both orally and visually. The receiver can ask for both visual and oral clarification. This interaction between sender and receiver makes it more likely that the message being sent will be received in the manner in which it was intended.

Nonverbal communication: In nonverbal communication, information is transmitted through pictures, 3-dimensional objects, facial expressions and actions. Another term for nonverbal communication is *body language*.

Clarifying the message: Being able to receive a message is just as important as being able to transmit one. Listeners must find out whether the message they heard and understood is the message the sender meant to give. Senders can also verify that what the listener heard is what they meant to say. Effective communication results when the listener receives the message in the same way that the speaker meant it.

Process Cue identifies the teaching strategy used for the activity. Descriptions are in the Teaching Strategies appendix.

Building Skills icons identify activities that provide skill-specific practice.

Sharpen the Skill suggests ideas for more skills practice.

4. VISUAL AND 2-WAY VERBAL COMMUNICATION

(AN EXPERIMENT ACTIVITY)

BUILDING Communication SKILLS

🕐 10 minutes ☀

MATERIALS
- Diagram for Visual and 2-Way Communication (1.3)
- masking tape or thumbtacks
- blank paper ☀

SHARPEN THE SKILL

COMMUNICATION—LISTENING
Before class, generate a detailed story about a "birthday celebration gone wrong." Describe the activities and the mishaps. Ask for 4 volunteers. Have 3 wait outside the classroom. Cue the remaining volunteer and the class with the word "listen." Tell the birthday story. Now invite 1 volunteer back in to hear the story from the 1st volunteer. Proceed until the story has been passed to the last volunteer. Ask students to discuss what happened and generate a list of tips for listening. ☀

Introduce experiment ●
Conduct an experiment involving both visual and 2-way verbal communication. Ask for a student volunteer to show the Diagram for Visual and 2-Way Verbal Communication to the class.

Students draw diagram
Distribute blank paper. Have the volunteer show the diagram to the class, explaining it and answering questions. Students should draw the diagram.

Discuss experiment ●
Post these final student drawings. Compare the results of the 3 experiments. Ask students: Which communication experiment was most successful? Why?

(Ongoing Assessment) Look for student understanding that the opportunity to interact as much as possible with the sender of a message improves the chances that the message will be understood the way it was intended.

DIAGRAM FOR VISUAL AND
2-WAY VERBAL COMMUNICATION

Outline format allows you to easily find your place while teaching.

Reduced **Activity Sheets** or **Transparencies** are provided. Full-size masters are at the back of the book.

8   *Comprehensive Health for the Middle Grades*

ANATOMY OF A UNIT

SPECIAL FEATURES

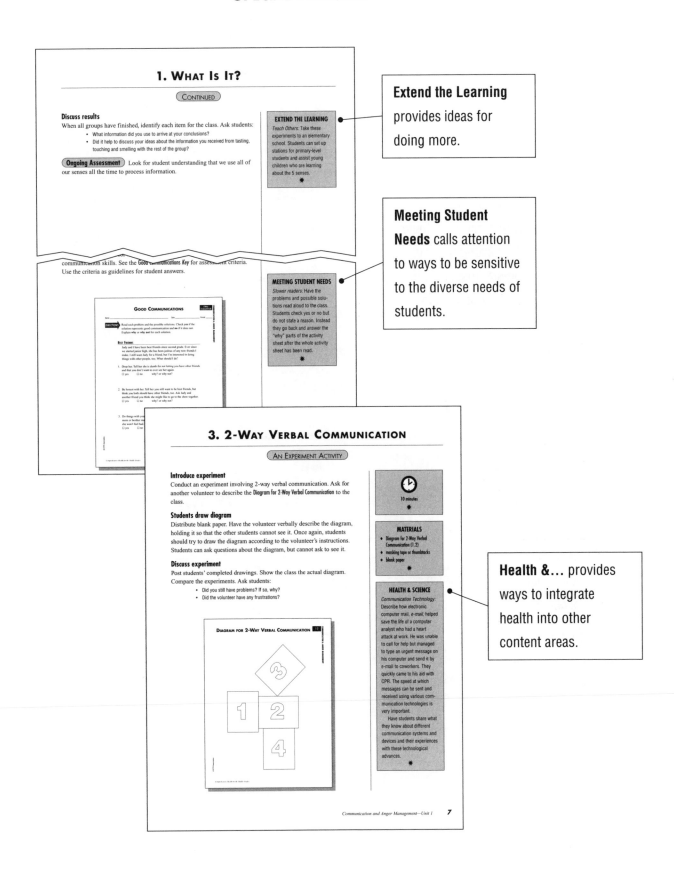

1. WHAT IS IT?

(CONTINUED)

Discuss results
When all groups have finished, identify each item for the class. Ask students:
- What information did you use to arrive at your conclusions?
- Did it help to discuss your ideas about the information you received from tasting, touching and smelling with the rest of the group?

(Ongoing Assessment) Look for student understanding that we use all of our senses all the time to process information.

EXTEND THE LEARNING
Teach Others: Take these experiments to an elementary school. Students can set up stations for primary-level students and assist young children who are learning about the 5 senses.

Extend the Learning provides ideas for doing more.

communication skills. See the *Good Communications Key* for assessment criteria. Use the criteria as guidelines for student answers.

MEETING STUDENT NEEDS
Slower readers: Have the problems and possible solutions read aloud to the class. Students check yes or no but do not state a reason. Instead they go back and answer the "why" parts of the activity sheet after the whole activity sheet has been read.

Meeting Student Needs calls attention to ways to be sensitive to the diverse needs of students.

GOOD COMMUNICATIONS

3. 2-WAY VERBAL COMMUNICATION

(AN EXPERIMENT ACTIVITY)

Introduce experiment
Conduct an experiment involving 2-way verbal communication. Ask for another volunteer to describe the *Diagram for 2-Way Verbal Communication* to the class.

Students draw diagram
Distribute blank paper. Have the volunteer verbally describe the diagram, holding it so that the other students cannot see it. Once again, students should try to draw the diagram according to the volunteer's instructions. Students can ask questions about the diagram, but cannot ask to see it.

Discuss experiment
Post students' completed drawings. Show the class the actual diagram. Compare the experiments. Ask students:
- Did you still have problems? If so, why?
- Did the volunteer have any frustrations?

10 minutes

MATERIALS
- Diagram for 2-Way Verbal Communication (1.2)
- masking tape or thumbtacks
- blank paper

HEALTH & SCIENCE
Communication Technology: Describe how electronic computer mail, *e-mail*, helped save the life of a computer analyst who had a heart attack at work. He was unable to call for help but managed to type an urgent message on his computer and send it by e-mail to coworkers. They quickly came to his aid with CPR. The speed at which messages can be sent and received using various communication technologies is very important.
Have students share what they know about different communication systems and devices and their experiences with these technological advances.

Health &... provides ways to integrate health into other content areas.

DIAGRAM FOR 2-WAY VERBAL COMMUNICATION

ANATOMY OF A UNIT

FAMILY INVOLVEMENT

Family Activities allow skills and knowledge to be reinforced at home.

Reduced Family Letters and/or **Activity Sheets** are provided. Full-size masters are in the back of the book.

Family Link offers ideas for additional family involvement.

Community Link suggests ways to reach outside the classroom.

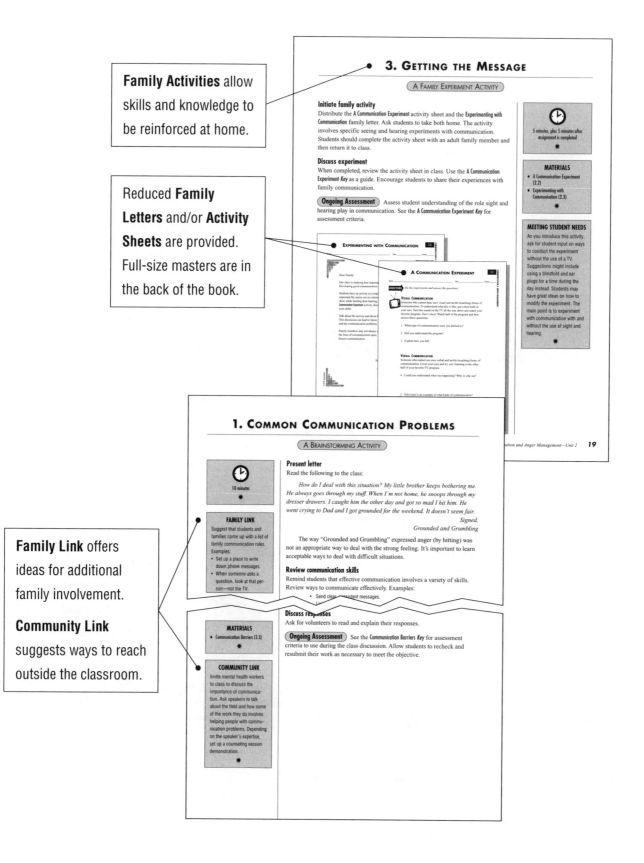

3. GETTING THE MESSAGE

A FAMILY EXPERIMENT ACTIVITY

Initiate family activity

Distribute the *A Communication Experiment* activity sheet and the *Experimenting with Communication* family letter. Ask students to take both home. The activity involves specific seeing and hearing experiments with communication. Students should complete the activity sheet with an adult family member and then return it to class.

Discuss experiment

When completed, review the activity sheet in class. Use the *A Communication Experiment Key* as a guide. Encourage students to share their experiences with family communication.

Ongoing Assessment   Assess student understanding of the role sight and hearing play in communication. See the *A Communication Experiment Key* for assessment criteria.

5 minutes, plus 5 minutes after assignment is completed

MATERIALS
- A Communication Experiment (2.2)
- Experimenting with Communication (2.3)

MEETING STUDENT NEEDS
As you introduce this activity, ask for student input on ways to conduct the experiment without the use of a TV. Suggestions might include using a blindfold and ear plugs for a time during the day instead. Students may have great ideas on how to modify the experiment. The main point is to experiment with communication with and without the use of sight and hearing.

EXPERIMENTING WITH COMMUNICATION

A COMMUNICATION EXPERIMENT

1. COMMON COMMUNICATION PROBLEMS

A BRAINSTORMING ACTIVITY

10 minutes

FAMILY LINK
Suggest that students and families come up with a list of family communication rules. Examples:
- Set up a place to write down phone messages.
- When someone asks a question, look at that person—not the TV.

MATERIALS
- Communication Barriers (3.3)

COMMUNITY LINK
Invite mental health workers to class to discuss the importance of communication. Ask speakers to talk about the field and how some of the work they do involves helping people with communication problems. Depending on the speaker's expertise, set up a counseling session demonstration.

Present letter

Read the following to the class:

How do I deal with this situation? My little brother keeps bothering me. He always goes through my stuff. When I'm not home, he snoops through my dresser drawers. I caught him the other day and got so mad I hit him. He went crying to Dad and I got grounded for the weekend. It doesn't seem fair.

Signed,
Grounded and Grumbling

The way "Grounded and Grumbling" expressed anger (by hitting) was not an appropriate way to deal with the strong feeling. It's important to learn acceptable ways to deal with difficult situations.

Review communication skills

Remind students that effective communication involves a variety of skills. Review ways to communicate effectively. Examples:

- Send clear, consistent messages.

Discuss responses

Ask for volunteers to read and explain their responses.

Ongoing Assessment   See the *Communication Barriers Key* for assessment criteria to use during the class discussion. Allow students to recheck and resubmit their work as necessary to meet the objective.

ANATOMY OF A UNIT

EVALUATION FEATURES

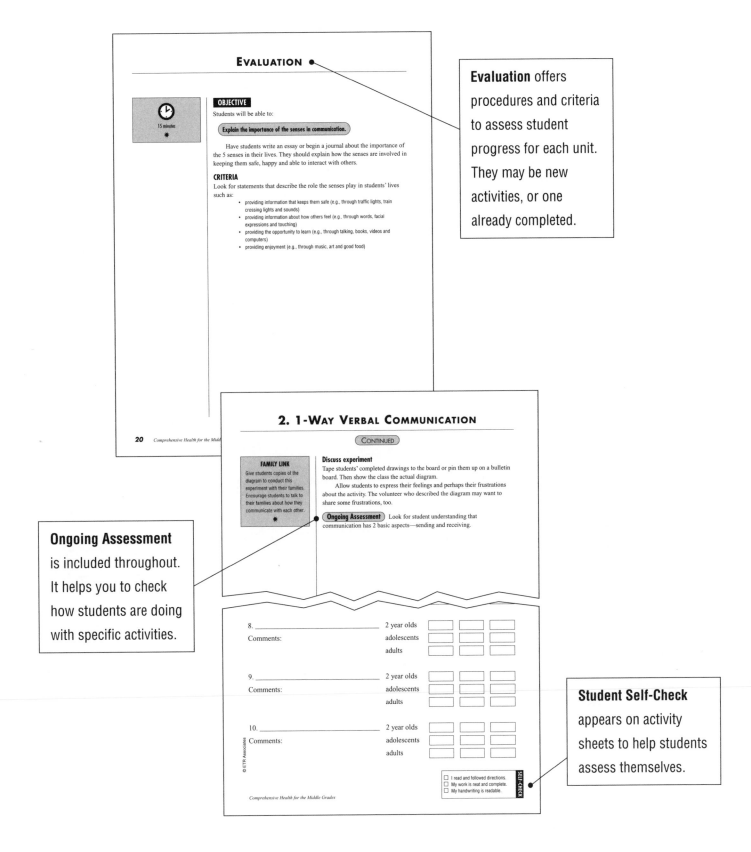

EVALUATION •

OBJECTIVE
Students will be able to:

Explain the importance of the senses in communication.

Have students write an essay or begin a journal about the importance of the 5 senses in their lives. They should explain how the senses are involved in keeping them safe, happy and able to interact with others.

CRITERIA
Look for statements that describe the role the senses play in students' lives such as:

- providing information that keeps them safe (e.g., through traffic lights, train crossing lights and sounds)
- providing information about how others feel (e.g., through words, facial expressions and touching)
- providing the opportunity to learn (e.g., through talking, books, videos and computers)
- providing enjoyment (e.g., through music, art and good food)

15 minutes

Evaluation offers procedures and criteria to assess student progress for each unit. They may be new activities, or one already completed.

20 *Comprehensive Health for the Middle*

2. 1-WAY VERBAL COMMUNICATION

CONTINUED

FAMILY LINK
Give students copies of the diagram to conduct this experiment with their families. Encourage students to talk to their families about how they communicate with each other.

Discuss experiment
Tape students' completed drawings to the board or pin them up on a bulletin board. Then show the class the actual diagram.

Allow students to express their feelings and perhaps their frustrations about the activity. The volunteer who described the diagram may want to share some frustrations, too.

Ongoing Assessment Look for student understanding that communication has 2 basic aspects—sending and receiving.

Ongoing Assessment is included throughout. It helps you to check how students are doing with specific activities.

8. _____	2 year olds	☐	☐	☐
Comments:	adolescents	☐	☐	☐
	adults	☐	☐	☐
9. _____	2 year olds	☐	☐	☐
Comments:	adolescents	☐	☐	☐
	adults	☐	☐	☐
10. _____	2 year olds	☐	☐	☐
Comments:	adolescents	☐	☐	☐
	adults	☐	☐	☐

© ETR Associates

Student Self-Check appears on activity sheets to help students assess themselves.

☐ I read and followed directions.
☐ My work is neat and complete.
☐ My handwriting is readable.

SELF-CHECK

Comprehensive Health for the Middle Grades

WAYS OF COMMUNICATING

TIME

1 period

ACTIVITIES

1. Defining Communication

2. 1-Way Verbal Communication

3. 2-Way Verbal Communication

4. Visual and 2-Way Verbal Communication

WAYS OF COMMUNICATING

OBJECTIVES

Students will be able to:

> 1. Define communication.

> 2. Compare 3 types of communication.

GETTING STARTED

Have:

- masking tape or thumbtacks
- blank paper

Copy:

- Diagram for 1-Way Verbal Communication (1.1)
- Diagram for 2-Way Verbal Communication (1.2)
- Diagram for Visual and 2-Way Verbal Communication (1.3)

Copy for each student:

- Communication? What's That? (1.4)

SPECIAL STEPS

Optional: Mount the diagrams on cardboard or laminate to reduce wear.

UNIT OVERVIEW

PURPOSE

Information, thoughts, ideas and feelings can be transmitted in many ways. Communication is important to interpersonal relationships. This unit helps students define and refine the concept of communication, particularly the dynamic and interactive aspects of the process.

MAIN POINTS

* Communication involves getting correct information, thoughts and feelings from a sender to the receiver.
* Verbal communication uses speaking to transmit messages.
* Nonverbal communication, or body language, includes pictures, 3-dimensional objects, facial expressions and actions.
* Verbal communication may be 1-way, such as radio and television broadcasts, or 2-way, which allows for feedback.
* Effective communication between sender and receiver means that the listener received the message in the way the speaker meant to send it.
* The more ways in which a receiver can clarify information being sent, the better the chance the message will be understood in the way it was intended.

REVIEW

To increase your understanding of different types of communication, review **Methods of Communication** *Instant Expert* (p. 10) and **Communication? What's That?** *Key* (p. 11).

VOCABULARY

body language—facial expressions, body movement, posture, gestures, etc., that are clues to a person's thoughts and feelings.

communication—The ability to express thoughts, feelings and reactions and to exchange information among people.

nonverbal communication—The use of symbols, signs or body language to convey a message.

1-way verbal communication—The process of passing information with no opportunity for the receiver to provide feedback.

2-way verbal communication—The process of passing information between speaker and listener with limited feedback.

1. DEFINING COMMUNICATION

15 minutes

✸

MEETING STUDENT NEEDS

Set up or review class groundrules before the brainstorming session. Remind students that all opinions are valid. Students should not comment about or judge other students' ideas.

✸

Brainstorm meaning of *communication*

Conduct a brainstorming session to define communication. Give all students a chance to offer suggestions. Write key phrases or words on the board.

Create class definition

Decide on a definition as a class. Possible definition:

> *Communication means getting correct information, thoughts and feelings from 1 person to another.*

Discuss ways we share information

Write 1-WAY, 2-WAY, NONVERBAL and BODY LANGUAGE on the board. Ask students: How do we most often share information, thoughts and feelings with others? (by talking). Discuss different types of communication, using the **Methods of Communication** *Instant Expert* as a guide.

2. 1-WAY VERBAL COMMUNICATION

AN EXPERIMENT ACTIVITY

Introduce experiment

Conduct an experiment involving 1-way verbal communication. Ask for a student volunteer to come to the front of the class. Give the volunteer the **Diagram for 1-Way Verbal Communication**. Don't allow other students to see the diagram.

Students draw diagram

Distribute blank paper to the class. Have the volunteer verbally describe the diagram to the class, holding it so that the other students cannot see it. Students draw a diagram according to the volunteer's instructions, without asking any questions.

(continued...)

10 minutes

MATERIALS
- Diagram for 1-Way Verbal Communication (1.1)
- masking tape or thumbtacks
- blank paper

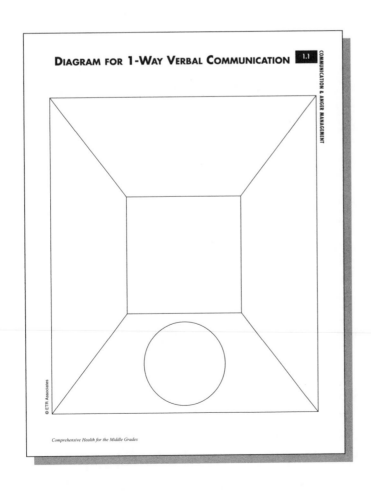

DIAGRAM FOR 1-WAY VERBAL COMMUNICATION 1.1

COMMUNICATION & ANGER MANAGEMENT

©ETR Associates

Comprehensive Health for the Middle Grades

2. 1-WAY VERBAL COMMUNICATION

CONTINUED

FAMILY LINK

Give students copies of the diagram to conduct this experiment with their families. Encourage students to talk to their families about how they communicate with each other.

Discuss experiment

Tape students' completed drawings to the board or pin them up on a bulletin board. Then show the class the actual diagram.

Allow students to express their feelings and perhaps their frustrations about the activity. The volunteer who described the diagram may want to share some frustrations, too.

Ongoing Assessment Look for student understanding that communication has 2 basic aspects—sending and receiving.

Introduce experiment

Conduct an experiment involving 2-way verbal communication. Ask for another volunteer to describe the **Diagram for 2-Way Verbal Communication** to the class.

Students draw diagram

Distribute blank paper. Have the volunteer verbally describe the diagram, holding it so that the other students cannot see it. Once again, students should try to draw the diagram according to the volunteer's instructions. Students can ask questions about the diagram, but cannot ask to see it.

Discuss experiment

Post students' completed drawings. Show the class the actual diagram. Compare the experiments. Ask students:

- Did you still have problems? If so, why?
- Did the volunteer have any frustrations?

10 minutes

MATERIALS

- Diagram for 2-Way Verbal Communication (1.2)
- masking tape or thumbtacks
- blank paper

HEALTH & SCIENCE

Communication Technology: Describe how electronic computer mail, *e-mail,* helped save the life of a computer analyst who had a heart attack at work. He was unable to call for help but managed to type an urgent message on his computer and send it by e-mail to coworkers. They quickly came to his aid with CPR. The speed at which messages can be sent and received using various communication technologies is very important.

Have students share what they know about different communication systems and devices and their experiences with these technological advances.

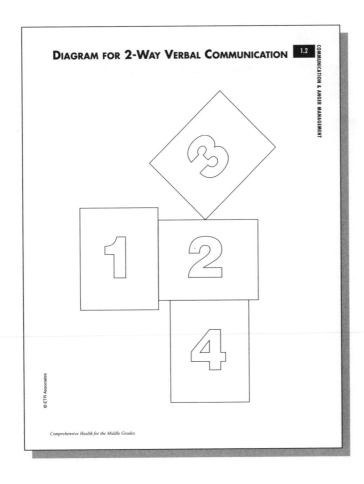

DIAGRAM FOR **2-WAY VERBAL COMMUNICATION** 1.2

© ETR Associates

Comprehensive Health for the Middle Grades

4. Visual and 2-Way Verbal Communication

10 minutes

MATERIALS

♦ Diagram for Visual and 2-Way Communication (1.3)
♦ masking tape or thumbtacks
♦ blank paper

SHARPEN THE SKILL

COMMUNICATION—LISTENING

Before class, generate a detailed story about a "birthday celebration gone wrong." Describe the activities and the mishaps. Ask for 4 volunteers. Have 3 wait outside the classroom. Cue the remaining volunteer and the class with the word "listen." Tell the birthday story. Now invite 1 volunteer back in to hear the story from the 1st volunteer. Proceed until the story has been passed to the last volunteer. Ask students to discuss what happened and generate a list of tips for listening.

Introduce experiment

Conduct an experiment involving both visual and 2-way verbal communication. Ask for a student volunteer to show the **Diagram for Visual and 2-Way Verbal Communication** to the class.

Students draw diagram

Distribute blank paper. Have the volunteer show the diagram to the class, explaining it and answering questions. Students should draw the diagram.

Discuss experiment

Post these final student drawings. Compare the results of the 3 experiments. Ask students: Which communication experiment was most successful? Why?

Ongoing Assessment Look for student understanding that the opportunity to interact as much as possible with the sender of a message improves the chances that the message will be understood the way it was intended.

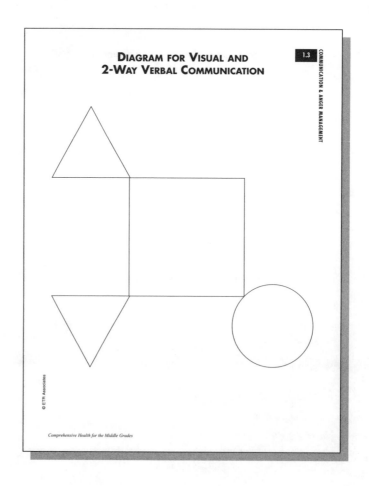

DIAGRAM FOR VISUAL AND
2-WAY VERBAL COMMUNICATION

1.3

COMMUNICATION & ANGER MANAGEMENT

© ETR Associates

Comprehensive Health for the Middle Grades

EVALUATION

OBJECTIVES

Students will be able to:

1. Define communication.

2. Compare 3 types of communication.

Distribute the **Communication? What's That?** evaluation sheet and ask students to complete it. They should write a definition of the word communication in terms that are meaningful to them, then describe a specific example of each type of communication as it occurs in their daily lives.

CRITERIA

See the **Communication? What's That?** *Key* for evaluation criteria. Allow students to resubmit the evaluation sheet if they have not yet met the objectives.

10 minutes

REVIEW
◆ Communication? What's That? *Key* (p. 11)

MATERIALS
◆ Communication? What's That? (1.4)

EXTEND THE LEARNING
Assign students to research various communication technologies, including the telephone, electronic books, computers, fax machines, video (TV), audio tapes, etc. Students should focus on the ability of the technology to allow people to interact. In reports, students could make predictions for the future.

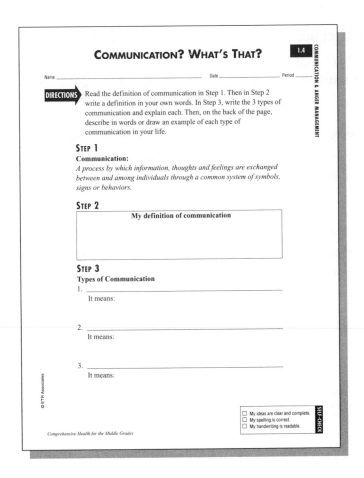

COMMUNICATION? WHAT'S THAT? `1.4`

Name _____ Date _____ Period ____

DIRECTIONS Read the definition of communication in Step 1. Then in Step 2 write a definition in your own words. In Step 3, write the 3 types of communication and explain each. Then, on the back of the page, describe in words or draw an example of each type of communication in your life.

STEP 1
Communication:
A process by which information, thoughts and feelings are exchanged between and among individuals through a common system of symbols, signs or behaviors.

STEP 2

My definition of communication

STEP 3
Types of Communication
1. _____
   It means:

2. _____
   It means:

3. _____
   It means:

☐ My ideas are clear and complete.
☐ My spelling is correct.
☐ My handwriting is readable.

`SELF-CHECK`

© ETR Associates

Comprehensive Health for the Middle Grades

METHODS OF COMMUNICATION

Communication is a process by which information is exchanged between and among individuals through a common system of symbols, signs or behaviors. Most communication is achieved verbally. Verbal communication can be *1-way* or *2-way*.

1-way verbal communication: In 1-way communication, information is passed from person to person with no opportunity for feedback. Most television and radio broadcasts are examples of 1-way communication. (There are exceptions, such as call-in radio and TV shows.)

    This type of communication does not allow the listener to ask the speaker questions that might clarify the message. It does not allow for interactions between and among people. When communication is 1-way, the message received may *not* be the message the speaker intended.

2-way verbal communication: Using this type of communication means that information passes orally from person to person with limited feedback. The receiver can ask for oral (verbal) clarification; he or she can ask questions of the speaker.

2-way verbal and visual communication: Information is passed both orally and visually. The receiver can ask for both visual and oral clarification. This interaction between sender and receiver makes it more likely that the message being sent will be received in the manner in which it was intended.

Nonverbal communication: In nonverbal communication, information is transmitted through pictures, 3-dimensional objects, facial expressions and actions. Another term for nonverbal communication is *body language*.

Clarifying the message: Being able to receive a message is just as important as being able to transmit one. Listeners must find out whether the message they heard and understood is the message the sender meant to give. Senders can also verify that what the listener heard is what they meant to say. Effective communication results when the listener receives the message in the same way that the speaker meant it.

KEY

 Read the definition of communication in Step 1. Then in Step 2 write a definition in your own words. In Step 3, write the 3 types of communication and explain each. Then, on the back of the page, describe in words or draw an example of each type of communication in your life.

STEP 1

Communication:

A process by which information, thoughts and feelings are exchanged between and among individuals through a common system of symbols, signs or behaviors.

STEP 2

My definition of communication

STEP 3

Types of Communication

1. _____

   It means:

2. _____

   It means:

3. _____

   It means:

UNIT
2

COMMUNICATION SENSE

TIME
1 period

ACTIVITIES
1. What Is It?
2. Communicating Without Words
3. Getting the Message

COMMUNICATION SENSE

OBJECTIVE

Students will be able to:

> Explain the importance of the senses in communication.

GETTING STARTED

Copy for each student:

- What Is It? (2.1)
- A Communication Experiment (2.2)
- Experimenting with Communication (2.3)

SPECIAL STEPS

Prepare experiment. See Activity 1 (p. 16).

PURPOSE

Communication is a dynamic process. It is both physical and mental. Investigating the role of the senses helps students understand the complexity of communication. Developing effective communication skills will help students maintain their health and well-being.

MAIN POINTS

All 5 senses (touch, taste, smell, hearing and seeing) are used to process information.

Most communication is visual and/or verbal.

Body language can visually communicate the sender's feelings. Sometimes body language speaks louder than words.

The senses provide us with information, enjoyment and the opportunity to learn new things.

REVIEW

To increase your comfort level with the visual and verbal communication experiment, review **A Communication Experiment Key** (p. 21).

VOCABULARY

body language—facial expressions, body movement, posture, gestures, etc., that are clues to a person's thoughts and feelings.

tactile communication—Nonverbal communication received through the sense of touch.

transmitters of information—Things which cause information to go between 1 person and another.

verbal communication—Transferring information, thoughts or feelings from 1 person to another by talking.

visual communication—Transferring information, thoughts or feelings from 1 person to another using the sense of sight.

1. WHAT IS IT?

25 minutes

MATERIALS

◆ What Is It? (2.1)
◆ items for the taste, touch and smell experiment

Introduce experiment

In our society, we get much of our information verbally or visually. However, we also receive information in other ways—through taste, touch and smell, as well as from hearing and seeing. Students will be conducting an experiment in communicating information through taste, touch and smell.

Groups conduct experiment

Divide the class into groups of 5–6. Distribute the **What Is It?** activity sheet and 4 items for the experiment to each group. Explain the group assignment:

• Try to identify each item in the paper bag or bottle individually (1-way communication). You cannot look at the items. You may use your other senses of smell, touch or taste.

• Discuss your guesses as a group (2-way communication). Come up with a group guess for each item.

(continued...)

TASTE, TOUCH AND SMELL EXPERIMENT

Use your imagination when selecting things for students to examine through taste, touch and smell. Provide at least 4 items for each group of 5–6 students. Be sure each group gets at least 1 item from each category. Place items in paper bags or unmarked bottles, as appropriate. Be sure students cannot identify the items by sight.

Suggestions include:

Taste	Touch	Smell
apples	Brussels sprouts	peppermint extract
potatoes (raw)	raisins	vinegar
jicama	yams	orange juice
onions	broccoli	vanilla extract
(If taste items are peeled,	kiwi fruit	
they will look similar.)	grapes	
	pasta	
	pine cones	
	leaves and flowers	

1. What Is It?

Discuss results

When all groups have finished, identify each item for the class. Ask students:

- What information did you use to arrive at your conclusions?
- Did it help to discuss your ideas about the information you received from tasting, touching and smelling with the rest of the group?

Ongoing Assessment   Look for student understanding that we use all of our senses all the time to process information.

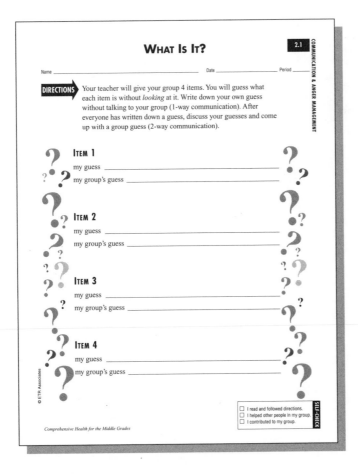

EXTEND THE LEARNING

Teach Others: Take these experiments to an elementary school. Students can set up stations for primary-level students and assist young children who are learning about the 5 senses.

2. COMMUNICATING WITHOUT WORDS

10 minutes

✴

MEETING STUDENT NEEDS

Be sensitive to conditions your students may have that make communication difficult. Do not allow these students to be singled out during the discussion. Stress that all of us have many ways in which we can communicate.

SHARPEN THE SKILL
COMMUNICATION—PROCESSING NONVERBAL COMMUNICATION

Show students a 15–20-second video clip of a person on a talk show, without the sound. What can they tell about the situation from the body language expressed? Replay the scene with sound. Discuss how well students read the body language cues. Repeat the activity with different video clips to demonstrate the role of nonverbal expression in communication.

Discuss communication difficulties

Discuss physical conditions that make it impossible for people to communicate in certain ways. A person who is blind cannot experience visual communication, but can experience verbal and tactile communication, communication through touching.

Ask students how a person who has a hearing problem might communicate (touching, sign language, writing, lip-reading and body language).

Demonstrate body language

Ask for volunteers to demonstrate various body positions or facial expressions. Other students should guess what is being communicated. For example: Folded arms and a tense body communicate a closed attitude; an open body position communicates a more open attitude.

A FAMILY EXPERIMENT ACTIVITY

Initiate family activity

Distribute the **A Communication Experiment** activity sheet and the **Experimenting with Communication** family letter. Ask students to take both home. The activity involves specific seeing and hearing experiments with communication. Students should complete the activity sheet with an adult family member and then return it to class.

Discuss experiment

When completed, review the activity sheet in class. Use the **A Communication Experiment** *Key* as a guide. Encourage students to share their experiences with family communication.

Ongoing Assessment
Assess student understanding of the role sight and hearing play in communication. See the **A Communication Experiment** *Key* for assessment criteria.

5 minutes, plus 5 minutes after assignment is completed

MATERIALS

♦ A Communication Experiment (2.2)
♦ Experimenting with Communication (2.3)

MEETING STUDENT NEEDS

As you introduce this activity, ask for student input on ways to conduct the experiment without the use of a TV. Suggestions might include using a blindfold and ear plugs for a time during the day instead. Students may have great ideas on how to modify the experiment. The main point is to experiment with communication with and without the use of sight and hearing.

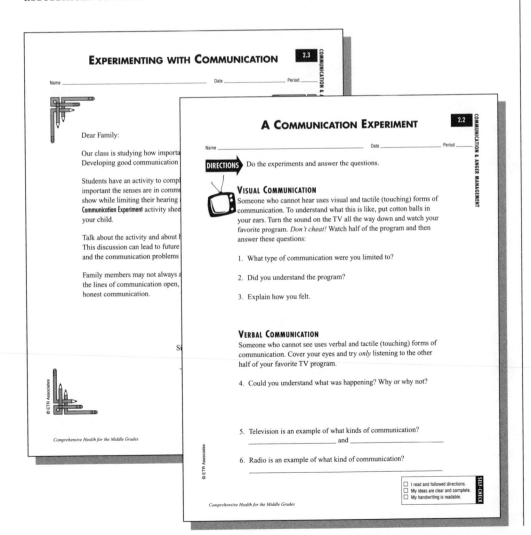

EXPERIMENTING WITH COMMUNICATION 2.3

Name _____ Date _____ Period _____

Dear Family:

Our class is studying how importa...
Developing good communication ...

Students have an activity to comp...
important the senses are in comm...
show while limiting their hearing ...
Communication Experiment activity shee...
your child.

Talk about the activity and about ...
This discussion can lead to future ...
and the communication problems ...

Family members may not always ...
the lines of communication open, ...
honest communication.

© ETR Associates

Comprehensive Health for the Middle Grades

A COMMUNICATION EXPERIMENT 2.2

Name _____ Date _____ Period _____

DIRECTIONS Do the experiments and answer the questions.

VISUAL COMMUNICATION
Someone who cannot hear uses visual and tactile (touching) forms of communication. To understand what this is like, put cotton balls in your ears. Turn the sound on the TV all the way down and watch your favorite program. *Don't cheat!* Watch half of the program and then answer these questions:

1. What type of communication were you limited to?

2. Did you understand the program?

3. Explain how you felt.

VERBAL COMMUNICATION
Someone who cannot see uses verbal and tactile (touching) forms of communication. Cover your eyes and try *only* listening to the other half of your favorite TV program.

4. Could you understand what was happening? Why or why not?

5. Television is an example of what kinds of communication?
   _____ and _____

6. Radio is an example of what kind of communication?
   _____

SELF-CHECK
☐ I read and followed directions.
☐ My ideas are clear and complete.
☐ My handwriting is readable.

© ETR Associates

Comprehensive Health for the Middle Grades

Communication and Anger Management—Unit 2 **19**

EVALUATION

15 minutes

OBJECTIVE

Students will be able to:

> **Explain the importance of the senses in communication.**

Have students write an essay or begin a journal about the importance of the 5 senses in their lives. They should explain how the senses are involved in keeping them safe, happy and able to interact with others.

CRITERIA

Look for statements that describe the role the senses play in students' lives such as:

- providing information that keeps them safe (e.g., through traffic lights, train crossing lights and sounds)
- providing information about how others feel (e.g., through words, facial expressions and touching)
- providing the opportunity to learn (e.g., through talking, books, videos and computers)
- providing enjoyment (e.g., through music, art and good food)

A COMMUNICATION EXPERIMENT

KEY

DIRECTIONS Do the experiments and answer the questions.

VISUAL COMMUNICATION

Someone who cannot hear uses visual and tactile (touching) forms of communication. To understand what this is like, put cotton balls in your ears. Turn the sound on the TV all the way down and watch your favorite program. *Don't cheat!* Watch half of the program and then answer these questions:

1. What type of communication were you limited to?   **visual**

2. Did you understand the program?   **Not very well**

3. Explain how you felt.
   It is hard to follow the story when you only see the action. I didn't know what was happening. I could only guess from the facial expressions.

VERBAL COMMUNICATION

Someone who cannot see uses verbal and tactile (touching) forms of communication. Cover your eyes and try *only* listening to the other half of your favorite TV program.

4. Could you understand what was happening? Why or why not?
   It was easier to follow the story when you could hear what was being said. But it was frustrating not being able to see facial expressions. Hearing made it easier to understand the communication.

5. Television is an example of what kinds of communication?
   __**1-way verbal (or oral)**__ and __**visual**__

6. Radio is an example of what kind of communication?
   __**1-way verbal**__

COMMUNICATION TROUBLES

TIME

2–3 periods

ACTIVITIES

1. I Don't Understand

2. Communication Solutions

3. Practice Overcoming Barriers

4. Communication Barriers

COMMUNICATION TROUBLES

OBJECTIVE

Students will be able to:

> Demonstrate techniques for overcoming barriers to communication.

GETTING STARTED

Make transparency of:

- I Don't Understand (3.1)
- Hints for Overcoming Barriers (3.2)

Copy for each student:

- Communication Barriers (3.3)

UNIT OVERVIEW

PURPOSE

Skillful communication requires knowledge and practice. This unit addresses some common barriers to effective communication and provides practice in overcoming them. Good communication is important in developing positive peer, family and community relationships.

MAIN POINTS

* Communication barriers can confuse the meaning of a message.

* Being able to identify personal communication barriers helps a person learn to listen and explain more carefully.

* Techniques for overcoming communication barriers include:
    * asking for more information
    * restating what was heard
    * explaining the situation
    * expressing feelings
    * staying calm by exhibiting a steady voice and calm body language

* Practicing techniques for overcoming barriers to communication helps people incorporate these techniques into their daily lives.

REVIEW

To increase your understanding of various barriers to effective communication, review **Communication Problems and Solutions** *Instant Expert* (p. 34) and **Communication Barriers** *Key* (p. 36).

VOCABULARY

clarification—The process of making an idea or thought clearer or easier to understand.

communication barriers—Anything which hinders clear communication between the sender and the receiver of a message.

overcoming barriers—Learning a new skill to replace a behavior which interferes with communication.

1. I DON'T UNDERSTAND

20 minutes

MATERIALS

♦ I Don't Understand (3.1)

Reflect on communication problems

Ask students to think of a disagreement with a family member or a friend and consider the reasons for the problem. Was the problem related to communication? Have them write down their ideas around the causes for the disagreement, but keep their responses to themselves for now.

Ask students:

- Why do we sometimes have trouble understanding other people?
- Why don't we always communicate clearly?

No matter how clearly people think they communicate, the actual messages received by others can be affected by many factors. Communication barriers may confuse the meaning of a message, but, with awareness, most communication barriers can be overcome.

(continued...)

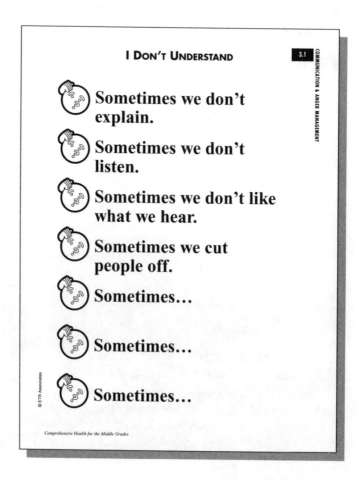

I DON'T UNDERSTAND   3.1

COMMUNICATION & ANGER MANAGEMENT

Sometimes we don't explain.

Sometimes we don't listen.

Sometimes we don't like what we hear.

Sometimes we cut people off.

Sometimes...

Sometimes...

Sometimes...

© ETR Associates

Comprehensive Health for the Middle Grades

Discuss barriers to communication

Display the I Don't Understand transparency. Reveal the statements 1 at a time, asking students if they can think of examples of that particular barrier. Students can share personal experiences if they wish. Key points:

- **Sometimes we don't explain things well.** We assume people understand us, and leave out information we think they already know. Or the words we use are too big, or we use too many slang words.
- **Sometimes we don't listen well enough.** It is very hard to be a good listener. Sometimes we concentrate so much on our own thoughts and feelings that we don't hear or understand someone else's. We are thinking about what we are going to say next instead of listening to what is being said now.
- **Sometimes we don't listen to others because we don't like or agree with what they are saying.** We decide that a person's point of view is not valid because it is different from our own.
- **Sometimes we cut people off.** We sometimes put people down; then they feel hurt or angry, so they stop trying to communicate or express a point of view. Or we interrupt or dominate the conversation, not letting anyone else talk.

Have students identify other communication barriers. List these barriers on the transparency as well.

Discuss how all of us create these barriers in our communication at some time or another, using the **Communication Problems and Solutions** *Instant Expert* as a guide. Stress the importance of being aware that these actions can block communication.

HEALTH & LANGUAGE ARTS

Journal writing: Have students keep a journal. Encourage them to write about how they communicate. Suggest that they write about personal examples of communication and reevaluate how well they communicate in different situations. Have them write in particular about how they communicate their feelings to others. At the end of the curriculum, have students summarize their progress in good communication in their journals.

2. COMMUNICATION SOLUTIONS

Give examples of overcoming barriers to communication

Display the Hints for Overcoming Barriers transparency. Reveal the statements 1 at a time as you discuss each idea.

Ask students for examples of each technique. Examples:

- **Ask for more information.** "I don't understand what that word means. Would you please explain further?"
- **Restate what you think you heard.** "Are you saying that…?"
- **Explain what you think happened.** "I feel that you cut me off in mid-sentence."
- **Tell your feelings.** "I get angry when I am put down for my opinions."
- **Try to stay calm.** "Could you explain that again, please?" Remember that attacking another person does not help you get your point across.

(continued...)

⏰ 10 minutes

✳

MATERIALS

◆ Hints for Overcoming Barriers (3.2)

✳

SHARPEN THE SKILL

COMMUNICATION—REMOVING POTENTIAL BARRIERS TO COMMUNICATION

Ask students to describe what they think would be the perfect circumstances for an important personal talk with another person.

✳

HINTS FOR OVERCOMING BARRIERS   3.2

 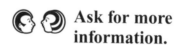 **Ask for more information.**

Restate what you think you heard.

Explain what you think happened.

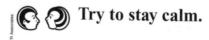 **Tell your feelings.**

Try to stay calm.

© ETR Associates

Comprehensive Health for the Middle Grades

2. COMMUNICATION SOLUTIONS

(CONTINUED)

Brainstorm ways to overcome barriers

Conduct a brainstorming session on statements or actions that will help overcome barriers. Use the **Communication Problems and Solutions** *Instant Expert* as a guide. Examples:

- Be considerate.
- Ask for clarification.
- Point out what you see as the barrier in a clear, calm voice.

SHARPEN THE SKILL
**COMMUNICATION—
ACCEPTING DIFFERENCES**

Ask students to generate solutions to common communication barriers by responding to the following prompt: "Other people can help me understand what they need, want or are saying by…."

3. PRACTICE OVERCOMING BARRIERS

**20 minutes,
plus time for presentations**

✱

MATERIALS

♦ Hints for Overcoming Barriers
   (3.2)

MEETING STUDENT NEEDS

Use small group activities to promote positive interactions among students. Encourage support for students with diverse levels of academic and social skills.

You can use different techniques to mix student abilities, gender and social skills. Use playing cards to sort randomly or draw names from a hat. Use different stickers on activity sheets to sort specifically. For example, all students with green dots are in a group.

Introduce roleplays

Display the Hints for Overcoming Barriers transparency. Explain that groups will plan and demonstrate for the rest of the class a roleplay of 1 way to deal with a communication problem. This problem could be a disagreement with a friend or family member, or a misunderstanding with a teacher.

Groups can use the communication problems group members wrote about in Activity 1 or the following situation:

A group of friends has decided to meet to go to a movie that starts at 6:00. It is almost 6:00 and 1 person has not arrived yet. The group starts to argue about whose fault it is and what to do about it.

(continued...)

HINTS FOR OVERCOMING BARRIERS | 3.2 | COMMUNICATION & ANGER MANAGEMENT

Ask for more
information.

Restate what you think
you heard.

Explain what you
think happened.

Tell your feelings.

Try to stay calm.

© ETR Associates

Comprehensive Health for the Middle Grades

Groups plan roleplays

Divide the class into groups of 4–5. Explain the group assignment:

- Choose a situation for the demonstration.
- Assign roles.
- Make sure the roleplay demonstrates at least 1 of the hints for overcoming barriers.
- Practice the roleplay at least once to make sure it demonstrates at least 1 of the steps for overcoming communication problems:
  - Asking for more information to understand the problem.
  - Restating what you think you understand the problem to be.
  - Explaining the situation from your point of view.
  - Expressing how you feel about a situation or problem.
  - Staying calm.
- Present the roleplay to the class.

Groups present roleplays

After groups present their roleplays, discuss each presentation. Did groups demonstrate at least 1 communication skill effectively?

Ongoing Assessment   Look for student presentations to demonstrate at least 1 of the following communication skills:

- asking for more information
- restating what was heard
- explaining the situation
- expressing feelings
- using a calm voice and body language

Allow students to redo their presentations based on assessment input.

SHARPEN THE SKILL
COMMUNICATION—INITIATING CONVERSATION

Ask students to generate appropriate requests for the opportunity for a serious talk with the following types of people:

- a parent
- a teacher
- a friend
- a younger sibling
- a store manager

4. COMMUNICATION BARRIERS

10 minutes

MATERIALS

♦ Communication Barriers (3.3)

COMMUNITY LINK

Invite mental health workers to class to discuss the importance of communication. Ask speakers to talk about the field and how some of the work they do involves helping people with communication problems. Depending on the speaker's expertise, set up a counseling session demonstration.

Describe reasons for communication problems

Distribute the Communication Barriers activity sheet. Have students work individually to apply what they know about communication barriers to the specific situations.

Discuss responses

Ask for volunteers to read and explain their responses.

Ongoing Assessment See the Communication Barriers *Key* for assessment criteria to use during the class discussion. Allow students to recheck and resubmit their work as necessary to meet the objective.

EVALUATION

OBJECTIVE

Students will be able to:

> **Demonstrate techniques for overcoming barriers to communication.**

Allow students to redo their roleplay presentations from Activity 3 if necessary to achieve the objective.

CRITERIA

Assess students' ability to demonstrate techniques for overcoming communication barriers. Look for behaviors such as the following:

- asking for more information
- restating what was heard
- explaining the situation
- expressing feelings
- using a calm voice and body language

COMMUNICATION PROBLEMS AND SOLUTIONS

We all have a different level of skill in expressing thoughts, feelings, beliefs and opinions. Sometimes messages are not clear. Poor communication can lead to misunderstandings and feelings of anger and frustration.

No matter how clearly people think they communicate, the actual messages received by others can be affected by many factors. Communication barriers may confuse the meaning of a message, but, with awareness, most communication barriers can be overcome.

COMMON COMMUNICATION PROBLEMS

Assuming: We often assume others understand our words, actions or even thoughts and feelings. When people assume others understand, important communication information is left out. Often we assume others understand slang, technical terms or a certain vocabulary. Effective communication is a critical aspect of education. Teachers need to be particularly clear about their assumptions related to terms and vocabulary.

Not listening: It is very hard to be a good listener. Sometimes we concentrate so much on our own thoughts and feelings that we don't hear or understand someone else's. We are thinking about what we are going to say next instead of listening to what is being said now. Listening skills are critical to good communication.

Not agreeing: Sometimes we cut off communication because we don't like or agree with what is being said. This is done in different ways. Some people just stop listening. Other people take the offensive and attack or discount a person or idea they don't agree with. Good communication allows and respects differences of opinion.

Dominating: Effective communication balances the flow of information. It is respectful of all involved. Interrupting, cutting people off and putting someone down tend to create hurt or angry feelings. This will often shut down communication completely. It is very difficult for someone to express a point of view if it clearly will not be respected.

(continued...)

COMMUNICATION SOLUTIONS

Gather information: Ask for more information. Check out the meaning of a word. Double check assumptions. When you feel information is not complete, check it out.

Restate: In your own words, restate information, thoughts or feelings. Ask if the communication was accurate. Use statements such as "Do you mean…?" or "Are you saying that…?"

Clarify problems: If you feel that communication was disrespectful or cut off, clarify what happened. Explain what you think occurred in the communication. For example, "I feel you cut me off in mid-sentence." Or, "I felt your use of slang was disrespectful."

Express your feelings: Let others know what your feelings are related to communication. If you feel hurt or angry or fearful, express it. For example, "I feel angry when I am put down for stating my opinion."

Stay calm and considerate: Attacking another person does not help you get your point across. Take deep breaths and remain calm and considerate.

COMMUNICATION SKILLS

Effective communication involves a variety of skills. These skills include the ability to:

- send clear, consistent messages
- listen carefully
- understand body language
- express thoughts, feelings and opinions
- remain calm, respectful and honest

When problems arise between and among people, the solution often lies in checking out the effectiveness of the communication. Examining a situation for each of these communication skills will help identify the issues and clarify the problem.

All of us create barriers in our communication at 1 time or another. The important thing is to be aware that these actions can block communication. We can learn to listen, explain more, be considerate and solve communication problems.

COMMUNICATION BARRIERS

KEY

 **DIRECTIONS** Write examples of the 4 barriers in the bubbles. See the example for the first barrier.

1. Sometimes we don't explain things well.

> We assume someone understands, and we leave out information we think they know.

> We use too many big words.

> We use slang words others don't understand.

2. Sometimes we don't listen well enough. It's very hard to be a good listener.

> We are so wrapped up in our own thoughts and feelings, we don't hear anyone else.

> We are thinking about what we are going to say next, instead of listening to what is being said at the moment.

3. Sometimes we tune others out when they are saying things we don't like or don't agree with.

> We decide that someone else's point of view is dumb, so we stop listening.

> We don't like what we are hearing, so we start thinking of other things.

4. Sometimes we cut people off.

> We interrupt.

> We put people down; then they feel hurt or angry and they stop trying to communicate.

> We dominate the conversation and don't let anyone else talk.

EMOTIONS AND COMMUNICATION

TIME
1–2 periods, with assignment to be completed before class

ACTIVITIES
1. Defining Emotions
2. Emotions Pictures

EMOTIONS AND COMMUNICATION

OBJECTIVE

Students will be able to:

> Conclude that emotions are very personal feelings, expressed differently from person to person.

GETTING STARTED

Assign:

- Defining Emotions (4.1), to be completed before this unit. See Activity 1 (p. 40).

Have:

- lined paper
- masking tape or thumbtacks

Copy for each student:

- Defining Emotions (4.1)

Copy:

- Emotions Pictures (4.2)–(4.11)

SPECIAL STEPS

Optional: Mount emotions pictures on cardboard or laminate to reduce wear.

UNIT OVERVIEW

PURPOSE

Emotions are a unique and important part of being human. Individuals express feelings in diverse and unique ways. An emotion cannot be seen; the expression of that emotion is our only clue to what a person is feeling. However, it is often difficult to interpret what emotion someone is feeling. To communicate and work effectively with a variety of people, students need to learn about the effects of emotions on communication.

MAIN POINTS

✳ Emotions or feelings are unique and very personal to individuals.

✳ Different individuals can express the same emotion in different ways.

✳ It's hard to accurately interpret a person's emotions just by observing behavior.

✳ Individuals need to learn how to express their feelings in socially acceptable ways.

REVIEW

To increase your comfort level with definitions of various emotions, review *Characterizing Emotions Instant Expert* (p. 44) and *Defining Emotions Key* (p. 45).

VOCABULARY

consensus—General agreement within a group concerning a certain idea.

criteria—A standard for judging a certain idea, thought, feeling or emotion.

diverse—Different; having various forms.

emotions—Feelings about or reactions to certain important events or thoughts.

facial expression—How the features of the face respond to emotions.

individual experience—Personally undergoing or observing something.

socially acceptable—Adequate enough to satisfy a standard.

unique—Being the only one of its kind.

1. DEFINING EMOTIONS

A CLASS DISCUSSION ACTIVITY

20 minutes

✸

MATERIALS
♦ Defining Emotions (4.1)

✸

MEETING STUDENT NEEDS

Social acceptability varies greatly from community to community and from culture to culture. However, generalities can usually be drawn about the social norms of a society, culture or community. Be sensitive to these norms and the potential for diversity among students.

✸

Research definitions

Distribute the **Defining Emotions** activity sheet before teaching this unit. Ask students to define the list of words.

Discuss definitions

When students have completed the activity sheet, discuss their responses using the **Characterizing Emotions** *Instant Expert* and the **Defining Emotions** *Key* as guides. Ask for volunteers to share their definitions with the class.

The way we express emotions communicates our feelings to other people. As we grow older, we learn to express emotions in ways that are socially acceptable and that improve our ability to communicate with family and friends.

Students form personal definition

Ask students to define social acceptability in their own terms, based on their own experiences and situations. Young people can look to family, religious leaders, counselors and community leaders, in addition to their friends, to help them define and refine the meaning of social acceptability.

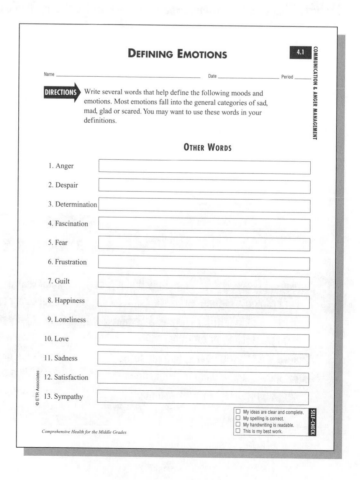

2. EMOTIONS PICTURES

A COOPERATIVE LEARNING GROUP ACTIVITY

Explain assignment

Divide the class into groups of 4–5. Give each group a piece of lined paper.
Explain the group assignment:

- Select a recorder to write down the group's responses during this activity.
- Recorders number the lined paper from 1 to 10.
- Decide what emotion is being expressed by each of the 10 Emotions Pictures. Groups must come to consensus on their decision.

Explain the following rules:

- Groups will move around the room to discuss each of the 10 Emotions Pictures.
- Only 1 group should look at a picture at a time.
- Talk only to the people in your group.
- Use the **Defining Emotions** activity sheet to help identify the emotions.

(continued...)

25 minutes

MATERIALS

- lined paper
- masking tape or thumbtacks
- Emotions Pictures (4.2)–(4.11)
- completed Defining Emotions (4.1), from Activity 1

SHARPEN THE SKILL

COMMUNICATION—EXPRESSING YOURSELF VERBALLY AND NONVERBALLY

Have students explore their own personal ways of expressing strong emotions by completing the following prompts:

- I show others my anger by…
- When I'm scared I…
- People can tell I'm sad or feeling low when I…

EMOTIONS PICTURE 1   4.2

© ETR Associates

Comprehensive Health for the Middle Grades

2. EMOTIONS PICTURES

CONTINUED

HEALTH & DRAMA

Have students use mime to act out selected emotions. Discuss the performances and clarify body language that was linked to a specific emotion.

Groups view pictures

Post the the Emotions Pictures in various spots around the room and tell groups to begin their work. Give 10 minutes to complete the activity.

Discuss group decisions

When groups are done, point to a picture and ask a group what emotion they think is being expressed. Ask other groups if they agree. If there is disagreement, find out what emotion the other groups chose. Ask groups to identify the criteria they used to make their choice.

Repeat the procedure for all of the pictures. There will not be agreement on every picture, and there are no right or wrong answers.

Facial expressions are important in the communication of emotions. Discuss what other clues can be used to identify another person's feelings (gestures, body language, tone of voice or tears).

EVALUATION

20 minutes

OBJECTIVE

Students will be able to:

> Conclude that emotions are very personal feelings, expressed differently from person to person.

Have students develop a creative writing piece entitled "My Feelings Are Mine." If written as an essay, it should be a few paragraphs long. It could also be a poem. It must, however, reflect the personal nature of emotions. Help students understand the activity by having them think about topics such as "What feelings tell me about myself and others" or "When I feel happy, sad, angry, I…."

CRITERIA

Look for introspection about the personal nature of emotions. Student writing should also indicate that it can be difficult to accurately interpret the emotions of others just by observing behavior.

CHARACTERIZING EMOTIONS

Emotions or feelings are very personal. Each of us draws upon individual experience to shape our understanding of emotions. Defining and redefining various emotions is a lifelong process. There are no right and wrong answers when we talk about feelings.

We can attempt to define the various emotions by describing general criteria that relate to them. For example, *happy* is generally considered a good or pleasant feeling. Smiles and laughter are often associated with being *happy*.

However, individuals express feelings in diverse and unique ways. An emotion cannot be seen; the expression of that emotion is our only clue to what a person is feeling. It is often difficult to interpret what emotion someone is feeling.

The following list describes some of the more common emotions:

anger: Hostile feelings because of opposition, a hurt, an injury.

despair: Loss of hope.

determination: A firm intention.

fascination: The state of being captivated, as by attraction, interest, terror.

fear: Anxiety caused by real or possible danger or pain.

frustration: Exasperation because of lack of achieving a goal or gratifying a desire.

guilt: A feeling of self-reproach from believing that one has done a wrong.

happiness: The state of being cheerful, joyful.

loneliness: The state of being unhappy because of lack of friends.

love: Strong affection or liking for someone or something.

sadness: The state of being unhappy, disappointed.

satisfaction: The state of being content, fulfilled.

sympathy: Mutual liking or understanding.

DEFINING EMOTIONS

KEY

 Write several words that help define the following moods and emotions. Most emotions fall into the general categories of sad, mad, glad or scared. You may want to use these words in your definitions.

OTHER WORDS

1. Anger — mad, rage, furious, hot under the collar, boiling, wrath, tantrum, grouchy, blow your top

2. Despair — hopeless, very sad, giving up, desperate, misery, depression

3. Determination — stubborn, decided on, intentions, resolved, not giving up

4. Fascination — interest, appeal, trance, daze, attraction

5. Fear — scared, afraid, fright, dread, feel "chicken," caution, horror, terror, panic, timid, anxious

6. Frustration — exasperation, stress, dissatisfied, unhappy, disappointment, grouchy

7. Guilt — shame, blame, remorse, regret, sorry

8. Happiness — cheer, contentment, delight, ecstasy, joy, enjoy, walking on air, bliss, elated, glad

9. Loneliness — being alone, sadness, missing people

10. Love — (have a) crush (on), like, adore, care about, affection, devotion, cherish

11. Sadness — unhappiness, disappointed, grief, misery, regret, loneliness, sorrow, heartache, broken heart

12. Satisfaction — contentment, delight, fulfilled, pleased, happy with, glad

13. Sympathy — liking, pity, caring, understanding, empathy

UNIT

5

FEAR AND ANGER

TIME
1 period

ACTIVITIES
1. The Stress Reaction
2. Expressing Anger

FEAR AND ANGER

OBJECTIVES

Students will be able to:

> **1. Explain the stress response.**

> **2. Describe appropriate ways to express anger.**

GETTING STARTED

Have:

- large coffee can containing several rocks

Make classroom set of:

- The Stress Reaction (5.1)

Copy for each student:

- Expressing Anger Checklist (5.2)
- Stress? Not Me! (5.13)

Make transparencies of:

- Expressing Anger (5.3)–(5.12)

SPECIAL STEPS

Select a student to help you with the experiment. See Activity 1 (p. 50).

UNIT OVERVIEW

PURPOSE

Strong emotions such as anger and fear cause physiological changes which have helped the human race survive for millions of years. This is the stress response. As students learn to manage stress and express powerful emotions in socially acceptable ways, they are better able to maintain their own health and well-being.

MAIN POINTS

* Strong emotions cause physical and mental changes in human beings.
* "Fight or flight" is a stress response that provides the body with extra energy and strength to protect itself.
* Stress is a common response to feeling fear and anger.
* People need to learn to express anger in socially acceptable ways.
* Physical exercise is an excellent way to deal with anger and manage stress.

REVIEW

To increase your understanding of the stress response and ways to deal with stress and anger, review **Stress, Fear and Anger** *Instant Expert* (p. 56) and **Stress? Not Me!** *Key* (p. 57).

V O C A B U L A R Y

adrenalin—A hormone secreted by the adrenal glands; important to the fight or flight response.

appropriate—Suitable for a particular occasion or situation.

fight or flight—A physical response to strong emotions or danger in which various body systems react to prepare for action.

pulse rate—The number of times the heart beats per minute.

secretion—A process by which a substance from certain cells is put to a new use elsewhere in the body.

stress—The feeling of being under pressure.

stressors—Anything that triggers a stress response.

tension—Mental, emotional or nervous strain.

1. THE STRESS REACTION

15 minutes

MATERIALS

♦ classroom set of The Stress Reaction (5.1)

♦ coffee can with rocks inside

✳

Discuss anger and fear

Ask students how they feel physically after they have been angry or afraid. Another way to describe this is feeling stress.

Feelings can affect us both mentally and physically. Part of being mentally healthy is knowing how to deal with our emotions. Knowing socially acceptable ways to express strong emotions is important both to communicate and to relieve tension and manage stress.

Distribute **The Stress Reaction** student reading page.

(continued...)

THE STRESS REACTION

STUDENT READING

5.1

COMMUNICATION & ANGER MANAGEMENT

Often when we are angry or frightened our bodies tense up. We may want to hit something (or someone) or run away. This is the stress reaction. It is also called "fight or flight."

During fight or flight, our bodies go through changes so we can respond to danger. This happens in all animals. Fight or flight gives animals the extra energy and strength they need to protect themselves.

WHAT HAPPENS DURING FIGHT OR FLIGHT?

During fight or flight the body releases a hormone called adrenalin. Adrenalin makes the heart beat faster and increases the breathing rate. Another hormone released at the same time causes the liver to produce sugar. This sugar provides energy for the body to use during fight or flight.

Other things also happen. The mouth becomes dry, the pupils of the eyes (the black part in the middle) become very large and the lungs can take in more air. You might notice that when you are upset or scared your stomach feels strange. This is because blood rushes away from the stomach to the other muscles in the body.

Sometimes people are able to perform amazing acts in life-threatening situations. They are able to do incredible things because of the extra energy produced during the fight or flight response. The body is able to perform at its very best—at its maximum capacity.

After the danger has gone, heartbeat and breathing go back to normal, blood returns to the stomach, blood sugar returns to a normal level and the body is able to relax.

WHAT IS STRESS?

The stress reaction doesn't just happen in response to physical danger. People may feel the fight or flight response when they become upset in traffic, want to win at sports, or feel nervous about taking a test or trying out for a play.

Sometimes people have problems or concerns that keep bothering them. Their bodies continue to react with fight or flight even though they are not really in danger. They are feeling *stress*. When people feel stress they have a difficult time relaxing. Too much stress can lead to mental problems and to physical problems such as ulcers.

There are many things that can cause us to feel upset or stressed. The things that cause stress are called *stressors*. It is important to learn how to relax to stay healthy and be happy. Some ways to relax also help manage stress and anger. These are exercising, taking deep breaths, meditating and talking about problems or worries with your family or close friends.

© ETR Associates

Comprehensive Health for the Middle Grades

---

1. The Stress Reaction

(CONTINUED)

Conduct experiment

Using the **Stress, Fear and Anger** *Instant Expert* as a guide, discuss how strong emotions such as fear and anger can stimulate mental and physical reactions, also known as stress.

Secretly arrange for the student helper to make an unexpected noise during this discussion. The student can drop something on the floor at the back of the room, such as a large coffee can with a few rocks in it. An unexpected slam of a classroom door will also work. This activity will work best if all eyes are on the teacher.

Discuss reactions

How did students react to the noise? (Students will probably react with the fight or flight response.) Explain that this is a response to stress. This is how stress "feels."

Ask students to check their pulse rates. They may feel their hearts pounding. However, their bodies will settle down quickly because it is obvious that there is no real danger.

Explain that our bodies react to surprise and to all strong emotions in the following ways:

- Adrenalin is released.
- Heart rate increases.
- Blood pressure rises.
- Stored sugar in the liver is released.
- Breathing rate increases.

Collect the student reading pages for reuse.

Ongoing Assessment) Look for student understanding that emotions often cause physical reactions. This is how the body responds physically to stress.

HEALTH & SCIENCE

Assign student research about instincts in different animals. Each student's report should focus on 1 animal. The instinctive animal behaviors should be fully described. Reports should draw conclusions about how this instinctive behavior helps the animal deal with the stress of staying alive in the environment.

2. EXPRESSING ANGER

A CLASS DISCUSSION ACTIVITY

25 minutes

✳

MATERIALS

- Expressing Anger Checklist (5.2)
- transparencies of Expressing Anger (5.3)–(5.12)

✳

Discuss ways to express anger

Ask students to describe ways they have seen people express anger.

Anger is a very powerful emotion that should not be denied. Everyone needs to learn how to release the tension of the feeling without hurting self or others or damaging things.

As people grow older, they are expected to learn how to deal with anger in socially acceptable ways. A tantrum from a 2 year old may be considered normal, but this behavior is not appropriate from someone who is 20.

Explain activity

Distribute the **Expressing Anger Checklist** activity sheet. Explain the assignment:

- Look at the pictures of various ways people express anger.
- For each picture, describe the illustrated behavior and check the box that indicates how appropriate you think this behavior is for a person of a certain age.
- Use the Comments section of the activity sheet to describe any "Maybe" responses.

(continued...)

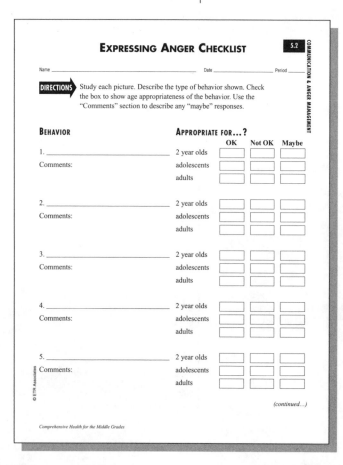

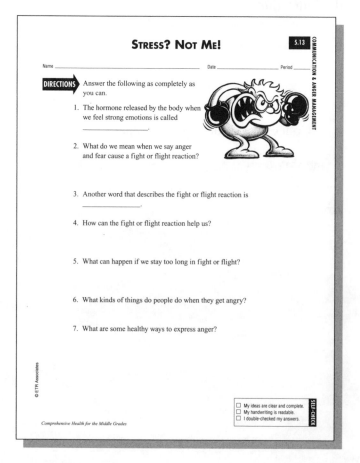

2. EXPRESSING ANGER

CONTINUED

Evaluate pictures

Display each **Expressing Anger** transparency. Have students fill in the activity sheet and then discuss their responses. The class should decide if the behavior is acceptable for 2 year olds, adolescents or adults. Repeat this process for all the pictures.

List acceptable expressions of anger

Ask students to suggest some positive ways to express anger. Exercise is an excellent way to deal with anger. Physical exercise uses up the sugar in the blood that was released by the liver.

Other physical ways to use up the sugar include:

- Beat up a pillow.
- Yell into a pillow at the top of your lungs.
- Participate in any active sport.
- Walk it off, talk it off or work it off.

Nonphysical ways to deal with anger include:

- Take time out (remove yourself from the situation).
- Stare into the distance.
- Take a deep breath.
- Tell someone how you feel.

All of these are usually acceptable ways of dealing with anger.

Optional: Have volunteers describe episodes where they expressed anger inappropriately and explain how they felt afterwards.

Ongoing Assessment Observe student behavior in and out of class to see how they deal with anger. Take time to acknowledge behaviors that are appropriate. Reinforcement of positive actions contributes to the development of important personal and social skills.

SHARPEN THE SKILL
STRESS MANAGEMENT— CLARIFYING PERSONAL EXPECTATIONS

Have students respond to the following writing prompt: "Any time I express strong feelings of anger, I would like to be able to say this about my words, attitudes and actions toward myself or others…"

COMMUNITY LINK

Have students make posters that "advertise" stress reduction tips. Post them around the school and community.

EVALUATION

REVIEW
- Stress? Not Me! *Key* (p. 57)

MATERIALS
- Stress? Not Me! (5.13)

OBJECTIVES

Students will be able to:

1. Explain the stress response.

2. Describe appropriate ways to express anger.

Distribute the **Stress? Not Me!** evaluation sheet and have students answer the questions. Discuss the answers as a class.

CRITERIA

Assess students' ability to describe the fight or flight response and healthy ways to express anger. See the **Stress? Not Me!** *Key* for evaluation criteria.

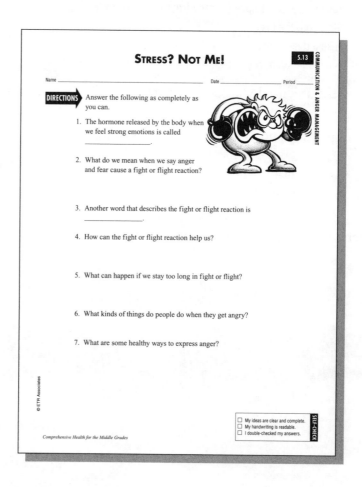

STRESS? NOT ME! — 5.13 — COMMUNICATION & ANGER MANAGEMENT

Name _____ Date _____ Period _____

DIRECTIONS Answer the following as completely as you can.

1. The hormone released by the body when we feel strong emotions is called _____.

2. What do we mean when we say anger and fear cause a fight or flight reaction?

3. Another word that describes the fight or flight reaction is _____.

4. How can the fight or flight reaction help us?

5. What can happen if we stay too long in fight or flight?

6. What kinds of things do people do when they get angry?

7. What are some healthy ways to express anger?

© ETR Associates

Comprehensive Health for the Middle Grades

SELF-CHECK
- ☐ My ideas are clear and complete.
- ☐ My handwriting is readable.
- ☐ I double-checked my answers.

STRESS, FEAR AND ANGER

Stress is a natural part of life. It is a physical reaction that is often related to feelings of fear or anger.

Frequently when human beings are angry or frightened their bodies tense up. They feel a strong urge to hit something (or someone) or to run away. This is a natural reaction that occurs in all animals. It is called the "fight or flight" response.

Fight or flight gives animals the extra energy and strength they need to protect themselves. When humans lived in the wild, the fight or flight response helped them stay alive. Now most humans no longer live in the wild, but they still experience the fight or flight response.

PHYSICAL CHANGES

To prepare itself to respond to danger, the body goes through changes during fight or flight. A hormone called adrenalin is released into the bloodstream. Adrenalin causes the heart to beat faster and increases breathing rate. Another hormone released at the same time causes the liver to produce sugar. This sugar provides energy for the the body to use during fight or flight.

Other physical responses take place as well. The mouth becomes dry, the pupils of the eyes become very large and the lungs can take in more air. Blood rushes away from the stomach to muscles elsewhere in the body, which is why the stomach can feel strange when a person gets upset or scared.

The fight or flight response enables the body to perform at maximum capacity. Sometimes people perform amazing acts in life-threatening situations. They are able to do incredible things because of the extra energy produced during the fight or flight response.

After the danger has passed, heartbeat and breathing go back to normal, blood returns to the stomach, blood sugar returns to a normal level and the body is able to relax.

(continued...)

STRESS, FEAR AND ANGER

THE RESPONSE TO STRESS

The body experiences the fight or flight reaction in response to both physical danger and mental or emotional upset. People may feel the fight or flight response when they become frustrated in traffic, want to win at sports, or feel nervous about taking a test or trying out for a play.

Sometimes people have problems or concerns that keep bothering them. Their bodies continue to react with fight or flight even though they are not really in danger. They are feeling *stress*. When people feel stress, they have a difficult time relaxing. Too much stress can lead to mental problems and to physical problems such as ulcers.

DEALING WITH STRESS AND ANGER

The things that can cause humans to feel upset or stressed are called *stressors*. For example, students may be fearful about an upcoming test. This is a stressor. Stress is not always "bad." In this case, the stress (fear) may motivate students to study.

Anger is another common source of stress. Learning socially acceptable ways to express anger is an important stress management tool. It is important to learn how to relax to stay healthy and be happy. Ways to manage stress and anger include exercising, taking deep breaths, meditating and talking about problems or worries with family or close friends.

KEY

 **DIRECTIONS** Answer the following as completely as you can.

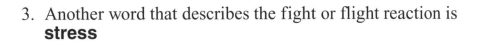

1. The hormone released by the body when we feel strong emotions is called **adrenalin**_____.

2. What do we mean when we say anger and fear cause a fight or flight reaction?
   When we feel afraid or angry adrenalin is released, and we may feel like running away or fighting.

3. Another word that describes the fight or flight reaction is **stress**_____.

4. How can the fight or flight reaction help us?
   It can protect us from danger. For example, it can cause us to jump out of the way of a speeding car.

5. What can happen if we stay too long in fight or flight?
   It can lead to physical problems like ulcers, mental problems, stress and the inability to relax.

6. What kinds of things do people do when they get angry?
   (answers will vary)

7. What are some healthy ways to express anger?
   • **Take a walk or jog—do something physical.**
   • **Scream into a pillow or in a place where you have privacy.**
   • **Take several deep breaths.**
   • **Remove yourself from the situation.**
   • **Tell someone how you feel.**

EMOTIONS BOOKLETS

TIME
1–2 periods

ACTIVITIES
1. My Emotions Booklet
2. Sharing Emotions

EMOTIONS BOOKLETS

OBJECTIVE

Students will be able to:

> Illustrate various expressions of emotions.

GETTING STARTED

Copy:

- Sample Emotions Booklet (6.1)

Copy for each student:

- Expressing Emotions (6.2)

SPECIAL STEPS

Construct a sample Emotions Booklet and gather booklet-making materials for students. See Activity 1 (p. 62).

UNIT OVERVIEW

PURPOSE

Emotions are personal and individual, as are the ways they are expressed. In this lesson, students illustrate situations that result in an emotional response, providing an opportunity for introspection and awareness of uniqueness.

MAIN POINTS

✳ Emotions and the way in which they are expressed are personal and unique to each individual.

✳ Each person reacts differently to different situations or things.

✳ The same emotional response can be evoked by many different types of experiences.

✳ There is no right or wrong emotional response; only the way in which the person expresses a feeling can be judged.

VOCABULARY

emotional response—The feeling experienced as a reaction to a situation or experience.

individuality—The sum of the characteristics that set a person or thing apart.

introspection—Looking into one's own mind, feelings, etc.

unique—Being the only one of its kind.

1. MY EMOTIONS BOOKLET

45 minutes

MATERIALS

- Sample Emotions Booklet (6.1)
- blank paper (colored is nice)
- crayons or markers
- scissors
- stapler
- *Optional:* a variety of magazines with pictures

MEETING STUDENT NEEDS

Students are challenged by this activity to be creative and introspective. Students' drawing ability varies greatly and should not be emphasized as the important aspect of the exercise. Students could also cut pictures from magazines to illustrate their booklets.

Show students the sample booklet

Explain that this activity gives students an opportunity to express their individuality. Because we are all unique, the things that cause 1 person to feel an emotion will not necessarily cause another person to feel the same emotion. Everyone reacts a little differently to situations. We enjoy different things, and we are disturbed by different things.

Describe procedure

List the various emotions students can use for their booklets on the board. Distribute 2 sheets of blank paper to each student. Students should cut and staple booklets before making their drawings. Explain how to make the booklets:

- Write an emotion on each page of the booklet. Write at least 6 emotions panels. You may use an emotion more than once.
- For each emotion panel, think of a situation that might cause someone to feel that emotion.
- Write a caption that describes the situation. The situation you describe can be made up, but it should be a situation that someone your age might experience.
- Think about and write down on the panel how the emotion might be expressed.
- Illustrate the situation. Stick figures are fine.
- Make a title page with your name, class and date.

Display student work

On a volunteer basis, discuss student work on the booklets. Read and post several examples.

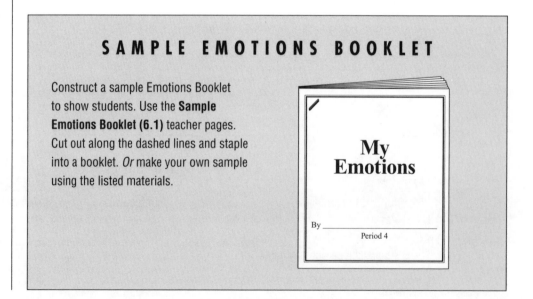

SAMPLE EMOTIONS BOOKLET

Construct a sample Emotions Booklet to show students. Use the **Sample Emotions Booklet (6.1)** teacher pages. Cut out along the dashed lines and staple into a booklet. *Or* make your own sample using the listed materials.

My
Emotions

By _____
Period 4

2. SHARING EMOTIONS

Initiate family activity

Distribute the **Expressing Emotions** family letter. Have students take the letter home along with their Emotions Booklets to share with their families. Ask students to talk with an adult family member about the emotions described in their booklets.

Family members can help students think about different ways to express the strong emotions that arise in various situations. This conversation may be personal in nature. Students should not be asked to share specifics in class.

10 minutes

MATERIALS

◆ completed Emotions Booklets, from Activity 1
◆ Expressing Emotions (6.2)

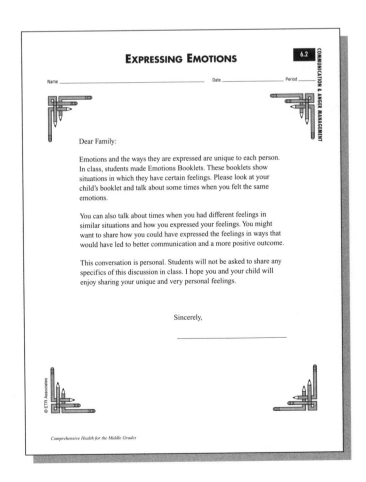

EXPRESSING EMOTIONS   6.2

Name _____ Date _____ Period _____

Dear Family:

Emotions and the ways they are expressed are unique to each person. In class, students made Emotions Booklets. These booklets show situations in which they have certain feelings. Please look at your child's booklet and talk about some times when you felt the same emotions.

You can also talk about times when you had different feelings in similar situations and how you expressed your feelings. You might want to share how you could have expressed the feelings in ways that would have led to better communication and a more positive outcome.

This conversation is personal. Students will not be asked to share any specifics of this discussion in class. I hope you and your child will enjoy sharing your unique and very personal feelings.

Sincerely,

_____

© ETR Associates

Comprehensive Health for the Middle Grades

EVALUATION

10 minutes

MATERIALS

♦ completed Emotions Booklets, from Activity 1

OBJECTIVE

Students will be able to:

> **Illustrate various expressions of emotions.**

When students have finished their booklets, let them share with class members if they don't mind others reading their work. Ask for students' observations about this activity. What did they learn about themselves and others? Congratulate students on their work and help them celebrate their individuality.

CRITERIA

Assess students' ability to illustrate a variety of feelings and expressions.

YOU AND YOUR FEELINGS ABOUT OTHERS

TIME

1 period

ACTIVITIES

1. Common Communication Problems

2. Explain the Problem

3. Offer a Solution

UNIT 7

YOU AND YOUR FEELINGS ABOUT OTHERS

OBJECTIVE

Students will be able to:

> Analyze common problems around communication in order to provide useful advice.

GETTING STARTED

Have:

- scissors
- lined paper

Copy for each student:

- Problem and Suggestion (7.1)

UNIT OVERVIEW

PURPOSE

Often, problems getting along with others are related to communication skills. In this lesson, students analyze common communication problems adolescents might have and make recommendations based on what they have learned. As students develop healthy ways to deal with emotions and express their feelings, they are better able to promote their own health and the health of others.

MAIN POINTS

* Getting along with others is related to effective communication skills.
* Individuals need to learn acceptable ways to deal with situations that cause strong emotions.
* Good communication skills help build positive relationships and improve interactions with others.

VOCABULARY

analyze—To examine in detail.

appropriate—Suitable for a particular occasion or situation.

communication skills—Anything that helps clear communication.

positive relationships—Balanced relationships built on trust and respect.

socially acceptable—Adequate enough to satisfy a standard.

1. Common Communication Problems

10 minutes

FAMILY LINK

Suggest that students and families come up with a list of family communication rules. Examples:

- Set up a place to write down phone messages.
- When someone asks a question, look at that person—not the TV.
- Use *I-statements* to express strong emotions.
- Don't yell from the other room with a question.
- Respect each other's feelings.

Present letter

Read the following to the class:

How do I deal with this situation? My little brother keeps bothering me. He always goes through my stuff. When I'm not home, he snoops through my dresser drawers. I caught him the other day and got so mad I hit him. He went crying to Dad and I got grounded for the weekend. It doesn't seem fair.

Signed,
Grounded and Grumbling

The way "Grounded and Grumbling" expressed anger (by hitting) was not an appropriate way to deal with the strong feeling. It's important to learn acceptable ways to deal with difficult situations.

Review communication skills

Remind students that effective communication involves a variety of skills. Review ways to communicate effectively. Examples:

- Send clear, consistent messages.
- Listen carefully.
- Understand body language.
- Express thoughts, feelings and opinions.
- Remain calm, respectful and honest.

When problems arise between and among people, the solution is often related to checking out the effectiveness of the communication.

List ways to express anger

Conduct a brainstorming session on some useful and socially acceptable ways to deal with the situation in the letter. List students' suggestions on the board. As the discussion progresses, students may want to add to and revise earlier suggestions. Help students see that the communication skills they have been learning will help build positive relationships and improve their interactions with friends, family and others.

Ongoing Assessment Look for students to understand that there are acceptable and unacceptable ways to deal with situations that cause strong emotions. Acceptable ways will build positive relationships with others.

2. EXPLAIN THE PROBLEM

Students identify problems

Distribute the **Problem and Suggestion** activity sheet. There are 2 parts. The first part has a place to write about a problem, and the second has a place to write a suggestion.

Explain that students will write about a specific concern or problem about getting along with others. It may be a real or fictional, but it should be something that students their age might face. It can involve friends, parents, brothers, sisters or teachers.

Other students will provide answers to the problem. Assure students that the name of the person who wrote the problem will not be known by the person providing a suggestion.

(continued...)

15 minutes

MATERIALS
◆ Problem and Suggestion (7.1)
◆ lined paper
◆ scissors

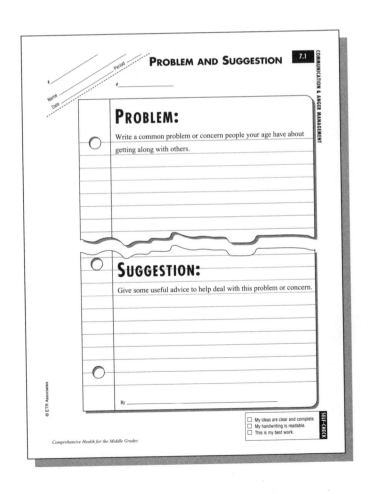

PROBLEM AND SUGGESTION   7.1

Name
Date   Period

PROBLEM:

Write a common problem or concern people your age have about getting along with others.

SUGGESTION:

Give some useful advice to help deal with this problem or concern.

By _____

☐ My ideas are clear and complete.
☐ My handwriting is readable.
☐ This is my best work.

Comprehensive Health for the Middle Grades

© ETR Associates

2. EXPLAIN THE PROBLEM

(CONTINUED)

HEALTH & LANGUAGE ARTS

Start a *Dear Gabby* newsletter or a *Dear Gabby* column in the school paper. Students should plan the process, including getting "real" questions from classmates. Set up an editorial process for answering questions and publishing the column. Establish an evaluation of this activity with a reader satisfaction survey.

Students write rough drafts

Distribute lined paper. Students can practice developing their problem or concern on this paper. Ask students to explain the situation fully, the way "Grounded and Grumbling" did in Activity 1.

Students finish descriptions

When students like how they have framed the problem, they should fill in Part 1 of the activity sheet. Collect activity sheets in such a way that the writer of each problem will not be identified. Students could print their problems or have friends write the problems so their handwriting cannot be identified.

Number the activity sheets in the corner and above the question. Then cut off and save the names.

3. OFFER A SOLUTION

Students give advice

Distribute the numbered **Problem and Suggestion** activity sheets from Activity 2 randomly to the class. Distribute lined paper. Ask students to use this paper to write some useful advice for the particular problem.

Groups analyze advice

When students have written down their ideas, divide the class into groups of 2–4. Explain the group assignment:

- Read and discuss the individual responses.
- Problem solve and analyze the situations with the group.
- You may choose a different response after group discussion.
- Write the group's suggestion in the appropriate place on each activity sheet and have each member sign.

Review suggestions

Collect the activity sheets when complete. Review the suggestions and make written comments, as appropriate. Before returning the activity sheets to the original writers, read a few to the class that have particularly helpful suggestions. *Note:* Do not give out any names when reading the selected activity sheets.

Ongoing Assessment Assess students' ability to provide useful and appropriate advice about a problem.

Depending on the problems identified, appropriate advice will include suggestions such as:

- Check to see if the message intended was the message received.
- Listen carefully.
- Watch for body language.
- Check out how you said something. What was your tone? Was it respectful?
- Have you been honest?
- Have you thought about feelings? yours? others?
- Has anger been expressed appropriately? If not, apologize.

15 minutes

MATERIALS

- prepared Problem and Suggestion (7.1), from Activity 2
- lined paper

EVALUATION

MATERIALS

- completed Problem and Suggestion (7.1), from Activity 3

✳

OBJECTIVE

Students will be able to:

> **Analyze common problems around communication in order to provide useful advice.**

Allow students to redo their responses on the **Problem and Suggestion** activity sheet if necessary to achieve the objective.

CRITERIA

Appropriate advice includes suggestions such as:

- Check to see if the message intended was the message received.
- Listen carefully.
- Watch for body language.
- Check out how you said something. What was your tone? Was it respectful?
- Have you been honest?
- Have you thought about feelings? yours? others?
- Has anger been expressed appropriately? If not, apologize.

FINAL EVALUATION

FINAL EVALUATION

Evaluate student learning

This assessment will help you evaluate student learning. It focuses on communication skills.

Distribute the **Good Communications** evaluation sheet and explain the assignment. The sheet describes 3 problems, each problem has 3 possible solutions. Students will analyze these age-appropriate dilemmas and possible solutions and determine which solutions use effective communication skills.

Students should check "yes" if the solution represents good communication skills, and "no" if it does not. For each situation, students should explain their answers.

CRITERIA

Assess students' work for their ability to identify and explain good communication skills. See the **Good Communications Key** for assessment criteria. Use the criteria as guidelines for student answers.

30 minutes

REVIEW

♦ Good Communications *Key* (p. 76)

MATERIALS

♦ Good Communications final evaluation

MEETING STUDENT NEEDS

Slower readers: Have the problems and possible solutions read aloud to the class. Students check yes or no but do not state a reason. Instead they go back and answer the "why" parts of the activity sheet after the whole activity sheet has been read.

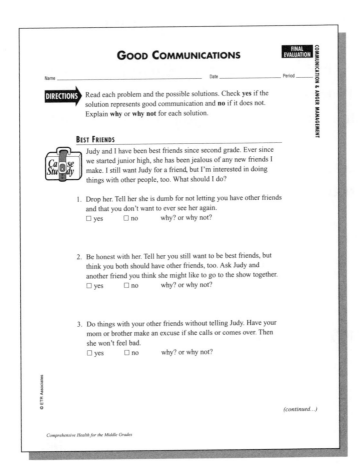

GOOD COMMUNICATIONS

FINAL EVALUATION

COMMUNICATION & ANGER MANAGEMENT

Name _____ Date _____ Period _____

DIRECTIONS Read each problem and the possible solutions. Check **yes** if the solution represents good communication and **no** if it does not. Explain **why** or **why not** for each solution.

BEST FRIENDS

Judy and I have been best friends since second grade. Ever since we started junior high, she has been jealous of any new friends I make. I still want Judy for a friend, but I'm interested in doing things with other people, too. What should I do?

1. Drop her. Tell her she is dumb for not letting you have other friends and that you don't want to ever see her again.
   ☐ yes ☐ no why? or why not?

2. Be honest with her. Tell her you still want to be best friends, but think you both should have other friends, too. Ask Judy and another friend you think she might like to go to the show together.
   ☐ yes ☐ no why? or why not?

3. Do things with your other friends without telling Judy. Have your mom or brother make an excuse if she calls or comes over. Then she won't feel bad.
   ☐ yes ☐ no why? or why not?

© ETR Associates

(continued...)

Comprehensive Health for the Middle Grades

GOOD COMMUNICATIONS

KEY

 Read each problem and the possible solutions. Check **yes** if the solution represents good communication and **no** if it does not. Explain **why** or **why not** for each solution.

BEST FRIENDS

 Judy and I have been best friends since second grade. Ever since we started junior high, she has been jealous of any new friends I make. I still want Judy for a friend, but I'm interested in doing things with other people, too. What should I do?

1. Drop her. Tell her she is dumb for not letting you have other friends and that you don't want to ever see her again.

   ☐ yes   ☑ no   why? or why not?

   Long-term friendships are important. Judy could be helped to understand that she is still important.

2. Be honest with her. Tell her you still want to be best friends, but think you both should have other friends, too. Ask Judy and another friend you think she might like to go to the show together.

   ☑ yes   ☐ no   why? or why not?

   Honesty is important in friendships. True friends can learn to hear the truth even if it is not exactly comfortable.

3. Do things with your other friends without telling Judy. Have your mom or brother make an excuse if she calls or comes over. Then she won't feel bad.

   ☐ yes   ☑ no   why? or why not?

   It is not honest. Judy will surely find out and be even more hurt.

(continued...)

GOOD COMMUNICATIONS

KEY, CONTINUED

AGE 13

I'm a 13-year-old boy who can't have any privacy, not even in the bathroom. I have 1 brother and 2 sisters and 1 bathroom. I'm the oldest. When I was little, people were always coming in and out of the bathroom when I took a bath. Now that I'm getting older, I think I have the right to lock the bathroom door. Whenever I do, my brother pounds on the door and screams until my mom or dad comes and makes me unlock the door. Then I get yelled at for locking the door and my brother laughs. What should I do?

1. When your parents aren't looking, beat up your brother. Tell him to shut up and leave you alone in the bathroom, or you'll beat him up again.

   ☐ yes ☑ no why? or why not?

   He will surely tell and you will get in trouble again. Anyway, fighting doesn't solve problems.

2. Pretend you don't care, then make sure to barge in on your brother whenever he's in the bathroom.

   ☐ yes ☑ no why? or why not?

   It will make him angry and tempers would flare again. Revenge doesn't solve problems any more than fighting.

3. Try to talk to your mom or dad. Tell them that you are growing up and would like privacy in the bathroom. Maybe you could work out a schedule so you could use the bathroom when it is not so busy. Ask your mom or dad to explain to your brother why you want privacy.

   ☑ yes ☐ no why? or why not?

   Honesty about your feelings and the reasons for your feelings is the key to good communication. Your parents will probably respond to this honest approach.

(continued...)

GOOD COMMUNICATIONS

KEY, CONTINUED

THE DANCE

I want to go to the school dance this weekend. My parents will let me go but I have to be home by 10:00. The dance isn't over until 11:00. I feel dumb when everyone else can stay till the end and I have to leave early. My parents treat me like a baby. What should I do?

1. Ask your parents if they would let you stay out later for this special occasion. Explain that the dance is supervised and you will leave the minute it is over. Tell them that you understand that they want you home early because they are concerned about you. But explain that this is a special occasion and many adults will be there.

   ☑ yes   ☐ no   why? or why not?

   Honesty and an agreed upon plan make sense. But it will only work as long as you keep up your end of the agreement.

2. Throw a tantrum. Tell your parents that they don't care about you or they would let you do what you want. Make them feel guilty.

   ☐ yes   ☑ no   why? or why not?

   You might not be allowed to go to the dance at all for expressing your anger in this way.

3. Don't tell your parents about the dance. Go spend the night with a friend and tell your parents you will be in by 10:00. What they don't know won't hurt them.

   ☐ yes   ☑ no   why? or why not?

   What if they find out? You can count on the fact that they will. Then you won't be trusted again for a long time.

APPENDIXES

Why Comprehensive School Health?

**Components of a
Comprehensive Health Program**

The Teacher's Role

Teaching Strategies

Glossary

Resources and References

WHY COMPREHENSIVE SCHOOL HEALTH?

The quality of life we ultimately achieve is determined in large part by the health decisions we make, the subsequent behaviors we adopt, and the public policies that promote and support the establishment of healthy behaviors.

A healthy student is capable of growing and learning; of producing new knowledge and ideas; of sharing, interacting and living peacefully with others in a complex and changing society. Fostering healthy children is the shared responsibility of families, communities and schools.

Health behaviors, the most important predictors of current and future health status, are influenced by a variety of factors. Factors that lead to and support the establishment of healthy behaviors include:

- awareness and knowledge of health issues
- the skills necessary to practice healthy behaviors
- opportunities to practice healthy behaviors
- support and reinforcement for the practice of healthy behaviors

The perception that a particular healthy behavior is worthwhile often results in young people becoming advocates, encouraging others to adopt the healthy behavior. When these young advocates exert pressure on peers to adopt healthy behaviors, a healthy social norm is established (e.g., tobacco use is unacceptable in this school).

Because health behaviors are learned, they can be shaped and changed. Partnerships between family members, community leaders, teachers and school leaders are a vital key to the initial development and maintenance of children's healthy behaviors and can also play a role in the modification of unhealthy behaviors. Schools, perhaps more than any other single agency in our society, have the opportunity to influence factors that shape the future health and productivity of Americans.

When young people receive reinforcement for the practice of a healthy behavior, they feel good about the healthy behavior. Reinforcement and the subsequent good feeling increase the likelihood that an individual will continue to practice a behavior and thereby establish a positive health habit. The good feeling and the experience of success motivate young people to place a high value on the behavior (e.g., being a nonsmoker is good).

From *Step by Step to Comprehensive School Health,* W. M. Kane (Santa Cruz, CA: ETR Associates, 1992).

COMPONENTS OF A COMPREHENSIVE HEALTH PROGRAM

The school's role in fostering the development of healthy students involves more than providing classes in health. There are 8 components of a comprehensive health education program:

- **School Health Instruction**—Instruction is the in-class aspect of the program. As in other subject areas, a scope of content defines the field. Application of classroom instruction to real life situations is critical.

- **Healthy School Environment**—The school environment includes both the physical and psychological surroundings of students, faculty and staff. The physical environment should be free of hazards; the psychological environment should foster healthy development.

- **School Health Services**—School health services offer a variety of activities that address the health status of students and staff.

- **Physical Education and Fitness**—Participation in physical education and fitness activities promotes healthy development. Students need information about how and why to be active and encouragement to develop skills that will contribute to fitness throughout their lives.

- **School Nutrition and Food Services**—The school's nutritional program provides an excellent opportunity to model healthy behaviors. Schools that provide healthy food choices and discourage availability of unhealthy foods send a clear message to students about the importance of good nutrition.

- **School-Based Counseling and Personal Support**—School counseling and support services play an important role in responding to special needs and providing personal support for individual students, teachers and staff. These services can also provide programs that promote schoolwide mental, emotional and social well-being.

- **Schoolsite Health Promotion**—Health promotion is a combination of educational, organizational and environmental activities designed to encourage students and staff to adopt healthier lifestyles and become better consumers of health care services. It views the school and its activities as a total environment.

- **School, Family and Community Health Promotion Partnerships**—Partnerships that unite schools, families and communities can address communitywide issues. These collaborative partnerships are the cornerstone of health promotion and disease prevention.

THE TEACHER'S ROLE

The teacher plays a critical role in meeting the challenge to empower students with the knowledge, skills and ability to make healthy behavior choices throughout their lives.

Instruction

Teachers need to provide students with learning opportunities that go beyond knowledge. Instruction must include the chance to practice skills that will help students make healthy decisions.

Involve Families and Communities

The issues in health are real-life issues, issues that families and communities deal with daily. Students need to see the relationship of what they learn at school to what occurs in their homes and their communities.

Model Healthy Behavior

Teachers educate students by their actions too. Students watch the way teachers manage health issues in their own lives. Teachers need to ask themselves if they are modeling the health behaviors they want students to adopt.

Maintain a Healthy Environment

The classroom environment has both physical and emotional aspects. It is the teacher's role to maintain a safe physical environment. It is also critical to provide an environment that is sensitive, respectful and developmentally appropriate.

Establish Groundrules

It is very important to establish classroom groundrules before discussing sensitive topics or issues. Setting and consistently enforcing groundrules establishes an atmosphere of respect, in which students can share and explore their personal thoughts, feelings, opinions and values.

Refer Students to Appropriate Services

Teachers may be the first to notice illness, learning disorders or emotional distress in students. The role of the teacher is one of referral. Most districts have guidelines for teachers to follow.

Legal Compliance

Teachers must make every effort to communicate to parents and other family members about the nature of the curriculum. Instruction about certain topics, such as sexuality, HIV or drug use, often must follow notification guidelines regulated by state law. Most states also require teachers to report any suspected cases of child abuse or neglect.

TEACHING STRATEGIES

The resource books incorporate a variety of instructional strategies. This variety is essential in addressing the needs of different kinds of learners. Different strategies are grouped according to their general education purpose. When sequenced, these strategies are designed to help students acquire the knowledge and skills they need to choose healthy behavior. Strategies are identified with each activity. Some strategies are traditional, while others are more interactive, encouraging students to help each other learn.

The strategies are divided into 4 categories according to their general purpose:

- providing key information
- encouraging creative expression
- sharing thoughts, feelings and opinions
- developing critical thinking

The following list details strategies in each category.

Providing Key Information

Information provides the foundation for learning. Before students can move to higher-level thinking, they need to have information about a topic. In lieu of a textbook, this series uses a variety of strategies to provide students the information they need to take actions for their health.

Anonymous Question Box

An anonymous question box provides the opportunity for all students to get answers to questions they might be hesitant to ask in class. It also gives teachers time to think about answers to difficult questions or to look for more information.

Questions should be reviewed and responded to regularly, and all questions placed in the box should be taken seriously. If you don't know the answer to a question, research it and report back to students.

You may feel that some questions would be better answered privately. Offer students the option of signing their questions if they want a private, written answer. Any questions not answered in class can then be answered privately.

Current Events

Analyzing local, state, national and international current events helps students relate classroom discussion to everyday life. It also helps students understand how local, national and global events and policies affect health status. Resources for current

TEACHING STRATEGIES

events include newspapers, magazines and other periodicals, radio and television programs and news.

Demonstrations and Experiments

Teachers, guest speakers or students can use demonstrations and experiments to show how something works or why something is important. These activities also provide a way to show the correct process for doing something, such as a first-aid procedure.

Demonstrations and experiments should be carefully planned and conducted. They often involve the use of supporting materials.

Games and Puzzles

Games and puzzles can be used to provide a different environment in which learning can take place. They are frequently amusing and sometimes competitive.

Many types of games and puzzles can be adapted to present and review health concepts. It may be a simple question-and-answer game or an adaptation of games such as Bingo, Concentration or Jeopardy. Puzzles include crosswords and word searches.

A game is played according to a specific set of rules. Game rules should be clear and simple. Using groups of students in teams rather than individual contestants helps involve the entire class.

Guest Speakers

Guest speakers can be recruited from students' families, the school and the community. They provide a valuable link between the classroom and the "real world."

Speakers should be screened before being invited to present to the class. They should have some awareness of the level of student knowledge and should be given direction for the content and focus of the presentation.

Interviewing

Students can interview experts and others about a specific topic either inside or outside of class. Invite experts, family members and others to visit class, or ask students to interview others (family members or friends) outside of class.

Advance preparation for an organized interview session increases the learning potential. A brainstorming session before the interview allows students to develop questions to ask during the interview.

TEACHING STRATEGIES

Oral Presentations

Individual students or groups or panels of students can present information orally to the rest of the class. Such presentations may sometimes involve the use of charts or posters to augment the presentation.

Students enjoy learning and hearing from each other, and the experience stimulates positive interaction. It also helps build students' communication skills.

Encouraging Creative Expression

Student creativity should be encouraged and challenged. Creative expression provides the opportunity to integrate language arts, fine arts and personal experience into a lesson. It also helps meet the diverse needs of students with different learning styles.

Artistic Expression or Creative Writing

Students may be offered a choice of expressing themselves in art or through writing. They may write short stories, poems or letters, or create pictures or collages about topics they are studying. Such a choice accommodates the differing needs and talents of students.

This technique can be used as a follow-up to most lessons. Completed work should be displayed in the classroom, at school or in the community.

Dramatic Presentations

Dramatic presentations may take the form of skits or mock news, radio or television shows. They can be presented to the class or to larger groups in the school or community. When equipment is available, videotapes of these presentations provide an opportunity to present students' work to other classes in the school and other groups in the community.

Such presentations are highly motivating activities, because they actively involve students in learning desired concepts. They also allow students to practice new behaviors in a safe setting and help them personalize information presented in class.

Roleplays

Acting out difficult situations provides students practice in new behaviors in a safe setting. Sometimes students are given a part to play, and other times they are given an idea and asked to improvise. Students need time to decide the central action of the situation and how they will resolve it before they make their presentation. Such activities are highly motivating because they actively involve students in learning desired concepts or practicing certain behaviors.

Sharing Thoughts, Feelings and Opinions

In the sensitive areas of health education, students may have a variety of opinions and feelings. Providing a safe atmosphere in which to discuss opinions and feelings encourages students to share their ideas and listen and learn from others. Such discussion also provides an opportunity to clarify misinformation and correct misconceptions.

Brainstorming

Brainstorming is used to stimulate discussion of an issue or topic. It can be done with the whole class or in smaller groups. It can be used both to gather information and to share thoughts and opinions.

All statements should be accepted without comment or judgment from the teacher or other students. Ideas can be listed on the board, on butcher paper or newsprint or on a transparency. Brainstorming should continue until all ideas have been exhausted or a predetermined time limit has been reached.

Class Discussion

A class discussion led by the teacher or by students is a valuable educational strategy. It can be used to initiate, amplify or summarize a lesson. Such discussions also provide a way to share ideas, opinions and concerns that may have been generated in small group work.

Clustering

Clustering is a simple visual technique that involves diagraming ideas around a main topic. The main topic is written on the board and circled. Other related ideas are then attached to the central idea or to each other with connecting lines.

Clustering can be used as an adjunct to brainstorming. Because there is no predetermined number of secondary ideas, clustering can accommodate all brainstorming ideas.

Continuum Voting

Continuum voting is a stimulating discussion technique. Students express the extent to which they agree or disagree with a statement read by the teacher. The classroom should be prepared for this activity with a sign that says "Agree" on one wall and a sign that says "Disagree" on the opposite wall. There should be room for students to move freely between the 2 signs.

As the teacher reads a statement, students move to a point between the signs that reflects their thoughts or feelings. The closer to the "Agree" sign they stand, the stronger their agreement. The closer to the "Disagree" sign they stand, the stronger their disagreement. A position in the center between the signs indicates a neutral stance.

Dyad Discussion

Working in pairs allows students to provide encouragement and support to each other. Students who may feel uncomfortable sharing in the full class may be more willing to share their thoughts and feelings with 1 other person. Depending on the task, dyads may be temporary, or students may meet regularly with a partner and work together to achieve their goals.

Forced Field Analysis

This strategy is used to discuss an issue that is open to debate. Students analyze a situation likely to be approved by some students and opposed by others. For example, if the subject of discussion was the American diet, some students might support the notion that Americans consume healthy foods because of the wide variety of foods available. Other students might express concern about the amount of foods that are high in sodium, fat and sugar.

Questioning skills are critical to the success of this technique. A good way to open such a discussion is to ask students, "What questions should you ask to determine if you support or oppose this idea?" The pros and cons of students' analysis can be charted on the board or on a transparency.

Journal Writing

Journal writing affords the opportunity for thinking and writing. Expressive writing requires that students become actively involved in the learning process. However, writing may become a less effective tool for learning if students must worry about spelling and punctuation. Students should be encouraged to write freely in their journals, without fear of evaluation.

Panel Discussion

Panel discussions provide an opportunity to discuss different points of view about a health topic, problem or issue. Students can research and develop supporting arguments for different sides. Such research and discussion enhances understanding of content.

Panel members may include experts from the community as well as students. Panel discussions are usually directed by a moderator and may be followed by a question and answer period.

Self-Assessment

Personal inventories provide a tool for self-assessment. Providing privacy around personal assessments allows students to be honest in their responses. Volunteers can share answers or the questions can be discussed in general, but no students should have to share answers they would prefer to keep private. Students can use the information to set personal goals for changing behaviors.

Small Groups

Students working together can help stimulate each other's creativity. Small group activities are cooperative, but have less formal structure than cooperative learning groups. These activities encourage collective thinking and provide opportunities for students to work with others and increase social skills.

Surveys and Inventories

Surveys and inventories can be used to assess knowledge, attitudes, beliefs and practices. These instruments can be used to gather knowledge about a variety of groups, including students, parents and other family members, and teachers.

Students can use surveys others have designed or design their own. When computers are available, students can use them to summarize their information, create graphs and prepare presentations of the data.

Developing Critical Thinking

Critical thinking skills help students analyze health topics and issues. These activities require that students learn to gather information, consider the consequences of actions and behaviors and make responsible decisions. They challenge students to perform higher-level thinking and clearly communicate their ideas.

Case Studies

Case studies provide written histories of a problem or situation. Students can read, discuss and analyze these situations. This strategy encourages student involvement and helps students personalize the health-related concepts presented in class.

TEACHING STRATEGIES

Cooperative Learning Groups

Cooperative learning is an effective teaching strategy that has been shown to have a positive effect on students' achievement and interpersonal skills. Students can work in small groups to disseminate and share information, analyze ideas or solve problems. The size of the group depends on the nature of the lesson and the make-up of the class. Groups work best with from 2–6 members.

Group structure will affect the success of the lessons. Groups can be formed by student choice, random selection, or a more formal, teacher-influenced process. Groups seem to function best when they represent the variety and balance found in the classroom. Groups also work better when each student has a responsibility within the group (reader, recorder, timer, reporter, etc.).

While groups are working on their tasks, the teacher should move from group to group, answering questions and dealing with any problems that arise. At the conclusion of the group process, some closure should take place.

Debates

Students can debate the pros and cons of many issues relating to health. Suggesting that students defend an opposing point of view provides an additional learning experience.

During a debate, each side has the opportunity to present their arguments and to refute each others' arguments. After the debate, class members can choose the side with which they agree.

Factual Writing

Once students have been presented with information about a topic, a variety of writing assignments can challenge them to clarify and express their ideas and opinions. Position papers, letters to the editor, proposals and public service announcements provide a forum in which students can express their opinions, supporting them with facts, figures and reasons.

Media Analysis

Students can analyze materials from a variety of media, including printed matter, music, TV programs, movies, video games and advertisements, to identify health-related messages. Such analysis might include identifying the purpose of the piece, the target audience, underlying messages, motivations and stereotypes.

TEACHING STRATEGIES

Personal Contracts

Personal contracts, individual commitments to changing behavior, can help students make positive changes in their health-related behaviors. The wording of a personal contract may include the behavior to be changed, a plan for changing the behavior and the identification of possible problems and support systems.

However, personal contracts should be used with caution. Behavior change may be difficult, especially in the short term. Students should be encouraged to make personal contracts around goals they are likely to meet.

Research

Research requires students to seek information to complete a task. Students may be given prepared materials that they must use to complete an assignment, or they may have to locate resources and gather information on their own. As part of this strategy, students must compile and organize the information they collect.

GLOSSARY

A

adrenalin—A hormone secreted by the adrenal glands, which are located near the kidneys. It is important to the fight or flight response.

analyze—To examine in detail.

anger—Hostile feelings because of opposition, a hurt, etc.

appropriate—Suitable for a particular occasion or situation; proper.

assertiveness—A component of communication in which individuals stand up for what they believe, want or need, without hurting or denying the rights of others.

B

body language—A form of nonverbal communication including facial expressions, body movement, posture, gestures, etc., that are clues to a person's thoughts and feelings.

C

clarification—The process of making an idea or thought clearer or easier to understand.

communication—The ability to express thoughts, feelings and reactions and to exchange information among people through a common system of symbols, signs or behaviors; involves both a sender and a receiver.

communication barrier—Anything which hinders clear communication between the sender and the receiver of a message; any type of interference that can confuse the meaning of the message being sent.

communication skill—Anything that helps clear communication between the sender and the receiver of a message.

consensus—General agreement within a group concerning a certain idea.

criteria—A standard for judging a certain idea, thought, feeling or emotion.

D

despair—Loss of hope.

determination—A firm intention.

displacement—A defense mechanism in which an individual transfers emotions from the true object to a less threatening substitute.

distress—A negative response to stress.

diverse—Different; having various forms.

Glossary

E

emotional response—The feeling a person experiences as a reaction to a situation or experience.

emotions—Feelings about or reactions to certain important events or thoughts; can be pleasant, unpleasant, uncomfortable or mixed.

F

facial expression—How the features of the face respond to emotions; a nonverbal gesture or clue which can convey how a person feels or thinks about a certain topic, idea or emotion. It is an aspect of body language.

fascination—The state of being captivated, as by attraction, interest, terror, etc.

fear—Anxiety caused by real or possible danger, pain, etc.

fight or flight—A physical response to strong emotions or danger in which various body systems react to prepare for action.

frustration—Exasperation because of lack of achieving a goal or gratifying a desire.

G

guilt—A feeling of self-reproach from believing that one has done a wrong.

H

happiness—The state of being cheerful, joyful, etc.

I

individual experience—Personally undergoing or observing something.

individuality—The sum of the characteristics that set a person or thing apart.

introspection—Looking into one's own mind, feelings, etc.

L

loneliness—The state of being unhappy because of lack of friends.

love—Strong affection or liking for someone or something.

M

mood—A person's sustained and predominant internal emotional experience (e.g., depression, euphoria).

N

nonverbal communication—The use of symbols, signs or body language to convey a message.

GLOSSARY

O

1-way verbal communication—The process of passing information from speaker to listener with no opportunity for the receiver to provide feedback of any kind.

overcoming barriers—Learning a new skill to replace a behavior which interferes with communication.

P

personality—Unique constellation of emotions, thoughts and behaviors that determine who a person is and how each person functions and adapts to life.

positive relationships—Balanced relationships built on trust and respect.

projection—A defense mechanism in which the individual attributes his or her own unacceptable feelings to someone else.

pulse rate—The number of times the heart beats in a given period.

S

sadness—The state of being unhappy, disappointed, etc.

satisfaction—The state of being content, fulfilled, etc.

secretion—A process by which a substance from certain cells is put to a new use elsewhere in the body.

self-esteem—Measure of how much a person values himself or herself.

socially acceptable—Adequate enough to satisfy a standard; satisfactory; appropriate.

stress—The feeling of being under pressure; bodily wear and tear caused by physical or psychological arousal by outside events.

stressors—Anything that triggers a stress response (e.g., external events, internal reactions or people).

sympathy—Mutual liking or understanding.

T

tactile communication—Nonverbal communication received through the sense of touch.

tension—Mental, emotional or nervous strain.

transmitters of information—Things which cause information to go between 1 person and another.

2-way verbal communication—The process of passing information between speaker and listener with limited feedback.

GLOSSARY

U

unique—Being the only one of its kind; different from others; without equal.

V

verbal communication—Transferring information, thoughts or feelings from 1 person to another by talking.

visual communication—Transferring information, thoughts or feelings from 1 person to another using the sense of sight.

RESOURCES AND REFERENCES

Resources

Video

Handling Emotions.
This video, especially designed for middle school students, explores the ups and downs of early adolescence, including mood swings and strong emotions. It suggests positive ways to express anger, sadness, depression and loneliness (30 minutes). Available from ETR Associates.

Books and Pamphlets

Mad Attitude?! Violence Gets You Nowhere. Santa Cruz, CA: ETR Associates.
This pamphlet gives young teens suggestions for cooling off their anger through exercise, discussion and other simple conflict resolution tactics.

Self-Esteem and Mental Health: Health Facts. N. J. Krantzler and K. R. Miner. Santa Cruz, CA: ETR Associates.
Books in the *Health Facts* series provide clear, concise background information on particular health topics, with an emphasis on topics and examples relevant to middle and high school students.

Self-Esteem ABC's. Santa Cruz, CA: ETR Associates.
This pamphlet uses a conversational tone to help adults encourage healthy attitudes in young people.

Teen Stress! And Ways to Handle It. Santa Cruz, CA: ETR Associates.
This upbeat pamphlet gives teens information on what stress is, what causes it, some negative reactions to it, and, most important, ideas for handling it.

RESOURCES AND REFERENCES

Organizations

American Mental Health Foundation
2 East 86th St.
New York, NY 10028
(212) 737-9027

American Psychological Association
1200 17th St. NW
Washington, DC 20036
(202) 955-7600

American Society for Adolescent
    Psychiatry
24 Green Valley Rd.
Wallingford, PA 19086
(215) 566-2773

National Center for Health Education
30 East 29th St.
New York, NY 10016
(212) 689-1886

National Council for Self-Esteem
California State Department of
    Education
P. O. Box 277877
Sacramento, CA 95827
(916) 455-6273

National Institute of Mental Health
Information Resources and Inquiries
    Branch
Parklawn Bldg., Room 15C-05
5600 Fishers Lane
Rockville, MD 20857
(301) 443-4513

RESOURCES AND REFERENCES

References

Bean, R. 1992. *Cooperation, social responsibility and other skills.* Santa Cruz, CA: ETR Associates.

Bean, R. 1992. *The four conditions of self-esteem.* 2d ed. Santa Cruz, CA: ETR Associates.

Dunne, G., D. Schilling and D. Cowan. 1990. *Impact! A self-esteem based skill development program for secondary students.* Santa Cruz, CA: ETR Associates.

Fetro, J. 1992. *Personal and social skills: Understanding and integrating competencies across health content.* Santa Cruz, CA: ETR Associates.

Gussin, G., and A. Buxbaum. 1984. *Self discovery: Developing skills.* Santa Cruz, CA: ETR Associates.

Krantzler, N. J., and K. R. Miner. 1994. *Self-esteem and mental health: Health facts.* Santa Cruz, CA: ETR Associates.

MASTERS

CONTENTS

DIAGRAM FOR 1-WAY VERBAL COMMUNICATION

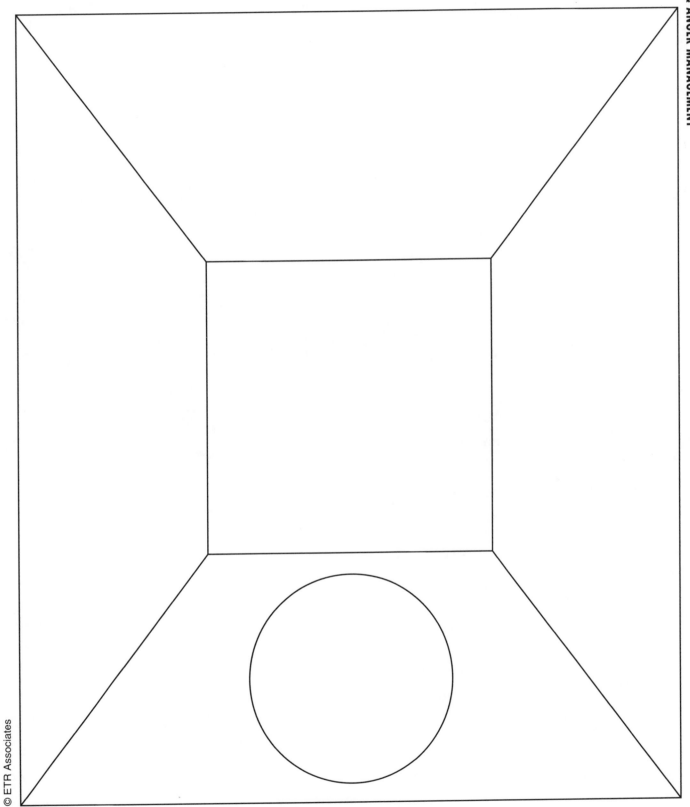

Comprehensive Health for the Middle Grades

DIAGRAM FOR 2-WAY VERBAL COMMUNICATION

DIAGRAM FOR VISUAL AND 2-WAY VERBAL COMMUNICATION

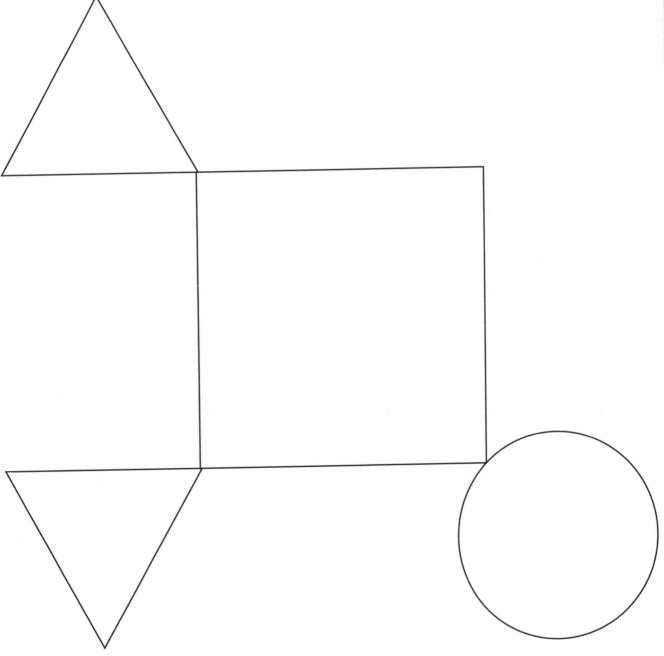

COMMUNICATION? WHAT'S THAT?

Name _____ Date _____ Period _____

DIRECTIONS Read the definition of communication in Step 1. Then in Step 2 write a definition in your own words. In Step 3, write the 3 types of communication and explain each. Then, on the back of the page, describe in words or draw an example of each type of communication in your life.

STEP 1

Communication:

A process by which information, thoughts and feelings are exchanged between and among individuals through a common system of symbols, signs or behaviors.

STEP 2

> **My definition of communication**

STEP 3

Types of Communication

1. _____

   It means:

2. _____

   It means:

3. _____

   It means:

☐ My ideas are clear and complete.
☐ My spelling is correct.
☐ My handwriting is readable.

SELF-CHECK

Comprehensive Health for the Middle Grades

WHAT IS IT?

Name _____ Date _____ Period _____

DIRECTIONS ▶ Your teacher will give your group 4 items. You will guess what each item is without *looking* at it. Write down your own guess without talking to your group (1-way communication). After everyone has written down a guess, discuss your guesses and come up with a group guess (2-way communication).

ITEM 1

my guess _____

my group's guess _____

ITEM 2

my guess _____

my group's guess _____

ITEM 3

my guess _____

my group's guess _____

ITEM 4

my guess _____

my group's guess _____

SELF-CHECK

- ☐ I read and followed directions.
- ☐ I helped other people in my group.
- ☐ I contributed to my group.

Comprehensive Health for the Middle Grades

A COMMUNICATION EXPERIMENT

Name _____ Date _____ Period _____

DIRECTIONS Do the experiments and answer the questions.

VISUAL COMMUNICATION

Someone who cannot hear uses visual and tactile (touching) forms of communication. To understand what this is like, put cotton balls in your ears. Turn the sound on the TV all the way down and watch your favorite program. *Don't cheat!* Watch half of the program and then answer these questions:

1. What type of communication were you limited to?

2. Did you understand the program?

3. Explain how you felt.

VERBAL COMMUNICATION

Someone who cannot see uses verbal and tactile (touching) forms of communication. Cover your eyes and try *only* listening to the other half of your favorite TV program.

4. Could you understand what was happening? Why or why not?

5. Television is an example of what kinds of communication?
   _____ and _____

6. Radio is an example of what kind of communication?
   _____

☐ I read and followed directions.
☐ My ideas are clear and complete.
☐ My handwriting is readable.

SELF-CHECK

Comprehensive Health for the Middle Grades

EXPERIMENTING WITH COMMUNICATION

Name _____ Date _____ Period _____

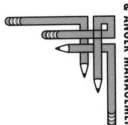

Dear Family:

Our class is studying how important communication is in our lives. Developing good communication skills is a lifelong task.

Students have an activity to complete to help them understand how important the senses are in communication. They watch a favorite TV show while limiting their hearing and sight, then fill out the **A Communication Experiment** activity sheet. Please share this experience with your child.

Talk about the activity and about how messages can be misunderstood. This discussion can lead to future discussions about communication and the communication problems that are common in families.

Family members may not always agree on everything. But by keeping the lines of communication open, you show that you believe in clear, honest communication.

Sincerely,

_____

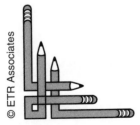

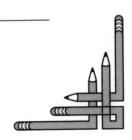

Comprehensive Health for the Middle Grades

I Don't Understand

 **Sometimes we don't explain.**

 **Sometimes we don't listen.**

 **Sometimes we don't like what we hear.**

 **Sometimes we cut people off.**

 **Sometimes...**

 **Sometimes...**

 **Sometimes...**

Comprehensive Health for the Middle Grades

Ask for more information.

 Restate what you think you heard.

 Explain what you think happened.

 Tell your feelings.

 Try to stay calm.

COMMUNICATION BARRIERS

Name _____ Date _____ Period _____

DIRECTIONS ➤ Write examples of the 4 barriers in the bubbles. See the example for the first barrier.

1. Sometimes we don't explain things well.

We use too many big words.

2. Sometimes we don't listen well enough. It's very hard to be a good listener.

3. Sometimes we tune others out when they are saying things we don't like or don't agree with.

4. Sometimes we cut people off.

SELF-CHECK

☐ My ideas are clear and complete.
☐ My spelling is correct.
☐ My handwriting is readable.

Comprehensive Health for the Middle Grades

DEFINING EMOTIONS

Name _____ Date _____ Period _____

DIRECTIONS ➤ Write several words that help define the following moods and emotions. Most emotions fall into the general categories of sad, mad, glad or scared. You may want to use these words in your definitions.

OTHER WORDS

1. Anger

2. Despair

3. Determination

4. Fascination

5. Fear

6. Frustration

7. Guilt

8. Happiness

9. Loneliness

10. Love

11. Sadness

12. Satisfaction

13. Sympathy

☐ My ideas are clear and complete.
☐ My spelling is correct.
☐ My handwriting is readable.
☐ This is my best work.

SELF-CHECK

Comprehensive Health for the Middle Grades

EMOTIONS PICTURE 1

Comprehensive Health for the Middle Grades

EMOTIONS PICTURE 2

Comprehensive Health for the Middle Grades

EMOTIONS PICTURE 3

Comprehensive Health for the Middle Grades

EMOTIONS PICTURE 4

EMOTIONS PICTURE 5

Comprehensive Health for the Middle Grades

EMOTIONS PICTURE 6

Comprehensive Health for the Middle Grades

EMOTIONS PICTURE 7

Comprehensive Health for the Middle Grades

EMOTIONS PICTURE 8

Comprehensive Health for the Middle Grades

EMOTIONS PICTURE 9

Comprehensive Health for the Middle Grades

EMOTIONS PICTURE 10

Comprehensive Health for the Middle Grades

THE STRESS REACTION

STUDENT READING

Often when we are angry or frightened our bodies tense up. We may want to hit something (or someone) or run away. This is the stress reaction. It is also called "fight or flight."

During fight or flight, our bodies go through changes so we can respond to danger. This happens in all animals. Fight or flight gives animals the extra energy and strength they need to protect themselves.

WHAT HAPPENS DURING FIGHT OR FLIGHT?

During fight or flight the body releases a hormone called adrenalin. Adrenalin makes the heart beat faster and increases the breathing rate. Another hormone released at the same time causes the liver to produce sugar. This sugar provides energy for the body to use during fight or flight.

Other things also happen. The mouth becomes dry, the pupils of the eyes (the black part in the middle) become very large and the lungs can take in more air. You might notice that when you are upset or scared your stomach feels strange. This is because blood rushes away from the stomach to the other muscles in the body.

Sometimes people are able to perform amazing acts in life-threatening situations. They are able to do incredible things because of the extra energy produced during the fight or flight response. The body is able to perform at its very best—at its maximum capacity.

After the danger has gone, heartbeat and breathing go back to normal, blood returns to the stomach, blood sugar returns to a normal level and the body is able to relax.

WHAT IS STRESS?

The stress reaction doesn't just happen in response to physical danger. People may feel the fight or flight response when they become upset in traffic, want to win at sports, or feel nervous about taking a test or trying out for a play.

Sometimes people have problems or concerns that keep bothering them. Their bodies continue to react with fight or flight even though they are not really in danger. They are feeling *stress*. When people feel stress they have a difficult time relaxing. Too much stress can lead to mental problems and to physical problems such as ulcers.

There are many things that can cause us to feel upset or stressed. The things that cause stress are called *stressors*. It is important to learn how to relax to stay healthy and be happy. Some ways to relax also help manage stress and anger. These are exercising, taking deep breaths, meditating and talking about problems or worries with your family or close friends.

EXPRESSING ANGER CHECKLIST

Name _____ Date _____ Period _____

DIRECTIONS ➤ Study each picture. Describe the type of behavior shown. Check the box to show age appropriateness of the behavior. Use the "Comments" section to describe any "maybe" responses.

BEHAVIOR

APPROPRIATE FOR...?

	OK	Not OK	Maybe
1. _____ 2 year olds	☐	☐	☐
Comments: adolescents	☐	☐	☐
adults	☐	☐	☐
2. _____ 2 year olds	☐	☐	☐
Comments: adolescents	☐	☐	☐
adults	☐	☐	☐
3. _____ 2 year olds	☐	☐	☐
Comments: adolescents	☐	☐	☐
adults	☐	☐	☐
4. _____ 2 year olds	☐	☐	☐
Comments: adolescents	☐	☐	☐
adults	☐	☐	☐
5. _____ 2 year olds	☐	☐	☐
Comments: adolescents	☐	☐	☐
adults	☐	☐	☐

(continued...)

EXPRESSING ANGER CHECKLIST

CONTINUED

BEHAVIOR	APPROPRIATE FOR...?	OK	Not OK	Maybe
6. _____	2 year olds	☐	☐	☐
Comments:	adolescents	☐	☐	☐
	adults	☐	☐	☐
7. _____	2 year olds	☐	☐	☐
Comments:	adolescents	☐	☐	☐
	adults	☐	☐	☐
8. _____	2 year olds	☐	☐	☐
Comments:	adolescents	☐	☐	☐
	adults	☐	☐	☐
9. _____	2 year olds	☐	☐	☐
Comments:	adolescents	☐	☐	☐
	adults	☐	☐	☐
10. _____	2 year olds	☐	☐	☐
Comments:	adolescents	☐	☐	☐
	adults	☐	☐	☐

☐ I read and followed directions.
☐ My work is neat and complete.
☐ My handwriting is readable.

SELF-CHECK

Comprehensive Health for the Middle Grades

EXPRESSING ANGER

1. Fight

Comprehensive Health for the Middle Grades

2. Swear

EXPRESSING ANGER

3. Scream

4. Cry

EXPRESSING ANGER

5. Break Things

Comprehensive Health for the Middle Grades

6. Take a Walk

EXPRESSING ANGER

7. Argue

Comprehensive Health for the Middle Grades

8. Talk About It

Comprehensive Health for the Middle Grades

9. Clam Up—Pout

Comprehensive Health for the Middle Grades

10. Exercise

STRESS? NOT ME!

Name _____ Date _____ Period _____

 **DIRECTIONS** Answer the following as completely as you can.

1. The hormone released by the body when we feel strong emotions is called _____.

2. What do we mean when we say anger and fear cause a fight or flight reaction?

3. Another word that describes the fight or flight reaction is _____.

4. How can the fight or flight reaction help us?

5. What can happen if we stay too long in fight or flight?

6. What kinds of things do people do when they get angry?

7. What are some healthy ways to express anger?

☐ My ideas are clear and complete.
☐ My handwriting is readable.
☐ I double-checked my answers.

SELF-CHECK

Comprehensive Health for the Middle Grades

SAMPLE EMOTIONS BOOKLET

My Emotions

By _____

Period 4

Happiness is…getting an "A" on your report card in Mr. Young's math class. I express it by running home to show my mom.

Satisfaction is…when you do something good for someone.
I express it by smiling.

Jealousy is…when your brother gets a new bike and you don't.
I sometimes express it by pouting.

Art provided by students from Faye Ross Junior High in Artesia, California.

(continued…)

Comprehensive Health for the Middle Grades

CONTINUED

Anger is...when your brother comes up and hits you for no reason.
I express this by hitting him back.

Anger is...when the TV screen goes blank when a good show is on.
I express my anger by pounding on the TV and turning the channels wildly until the picture comes back.

Anger is...the reaction you feel when you break a long fingernail.
I express it by yelling a lot at myself.

Happiness is...when you live in a 2-bedroom apartment and you share a room with your mom, then all of a sudden your brother moves out.
I express it by yelling "Yea!"

Art provided by students from Faye Ross Junior High in Artesia, California.

Comprehensive Health for the Middle Grades

EXPRESSING EMOTIONS

Name _____ Date _____ Period _____

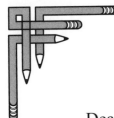

Dear Family:

Emotions and the ways they are expressed are unique to each person. In class, students made Emotions Booklets. These booklets show situations in which they have certain feelings. Please look at your child's booklet and talk about some times when you felt the same emotions.

You can also talk about times when you had different feelings in similar situations and how you expressed your feelings. You might want to share how you could have expressed the feelings in ways that would have led to better communication and a more positive outcome.

This conversation is personal. Students will not be asked to share any specifics of this discussion in class. I hope you and your child will enjoy sharing your unique and very personal feelings.

Sincerely,

_____

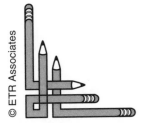
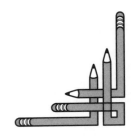

Comprehensive Health for the Middle Grades

#_____

Period_____

Name_____

Date_____

#_____

PROBLEM:

Write a common problem or concern people your age have about getting along with others.

SUGGESTION:

Give some useful advice to help deal with this problem or concern.

By _____

☐ My ideas are clear and complete.
☐ My handwriting is readable.
☐ This is my best work.

SELF-CHECK

Comprehensive Health for the Middle Grades

GOOD COMMUNICATIONS

Name _____ Date _____ Period _____

 **DIRECTIONS** Read each problem and the possible solutions. Check **yes** if the solution represents good communication and **no** if it does not. Explain **why** or **why not** for each solution.

BEST FRIENDS

Judy and I have been best friends since second grade. Ever since we started junior high, she has been jealous of any new friends I make. I still want Judy for a friend, but I'm interested in doing things with other people, too. What should I do?

1. Drop her. Tell her she is dumb for not letting you have other friends and that you don't want to ever see her again.

   ☐ yes   ☐ no   why? or why not?

2. Be honest with her. Tell her you still want to be best friends, but think you both should have other friends, too. Ask Judy and another friend you think she might like to go to the show together.

   ☐ yes   ☐ no   why? or why not?

3. Do things with your other friends without telling Judy. Have your mom or brother make an excuse if she calls or comes over. Then she won't feel bad.

   ☐ yes   ☐ no   why? or why not?

(continued...)

Comprehensive Health for the Middle Grades

GOOD COMMUNICATIONS

CONTINUED

AGE 13

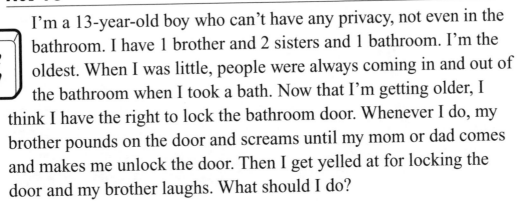

I'm a 13-year-old boy who can't have any privacy, not even in the bathroom. I have 1 brother and 2 sisters and 1 bathroom. I'm the oldest. When I was little, people were always coming in and out of the bathroom when I took a bath. Now that I'm getting older, I think I have the right to lock the bathroom door. Whenever I do, my brother pounds on the door and screams until my mom or dad comes and makes me unlock the door. Then I get yelled at for locking the door and my brother laughs. What should I do?

1. When your parents aren't looking, beat up your brother. Tell him to shut up and leave you alone in the bathroom, or you'll beat him up again.

   ☐ yes   ☐ no   why? or why not?

2. Pretend you don't care, then make sure to barge in on your brother whenever he's in the bathroom.

   ☐ yes   ☐ no   why? or why not?

3. Try to talk to your mom or dad. Tell them that you are growing up and would like privacy in the bathroom. Maybe you could work out a schedule so you could use the bathroom when it is not so busy. Ask your mom or dad to explain to your brother why you want privacy.

   ☐ yes   ☐ no   why? or why not?

(continued...)

Good Communications

Continued

The Dance

I want to go to the school dance this weekend. My parents will let me go but I have to be home by 10:00. The dance isn't over until 11:00. I feel dumb when everyone else can stay till the end and I have to leave early. My parents treat me like a baby. What should I do?

1. Ask your parents if they would let you stay out later for this special occasion. Explain that the dance is supervised and you will leave the minute it is over. Tell them that you understand that they want you home early because they are concerned about you. But explain that this is a special occasion and many adults will be there.

   ☐ yes   ☐ no   why? or why not?

2. Throw a tantrum. Tell your parents that they don't care about you or they would let you do what you want. Make them feel guilty.

   ☐ yes   ☐ no   why? or why not?

3. Don't tell your parents about the dance. Go spend the night with a friend and tell your parents you will be in by 10:00. What they don't know won't hurt them.

   ☐ yes   ☐ no   why? or why not?

☐ My work is neat and complete.
☐ My spelling is correct.
☐ My handwriting is readable.
☐ My work is neat and complete.